GCSE Health & Social Care
Teacher's Support Pack

Sue Morris, Marion Tyler and James O'Leary

Folens

© 2009 Folens Limited, on behalf of the authors.

United Kingdom: Folens Publishers, Waterslade House, Thame Road, Haddenham, Bucks, HP17 8NT.
Email: folens@folens.com
Website: www.folens.com

Ireland: Folens Publishers, Greenhills Road, Tallaght, Dublin 24.
Email: info@folens.ie
Website: www.folens.ie

Editor: Daniel Bottom
Text design and page layout: Sally Boothroyd
Cover design: Jump To!
Cover image: (left) © Monkey Business/Fotolia; (centre left) © Marzanna Syncerz/Fotolia; (centre right) © Moodboard/Fotolia; (right) © Monkey Business/Fotolia
Illustrations: Tony Randell

The websites recommended in this publication were correct at the time of going to press; however, websites may have been removed or web addresses changed since that time. Folens has made every attempt to suggest websites that are reliable and appropriate for students' use. It is not unknown for unscrupulous individuals to put unsuitable material on websites that may be accessed by students. Teachers should check all websites before allowing students to access them. Folens is not responsible for the content of external websites.

For general spellings Folens adheres to *Oxford Dictionary of English*, Second Edition (Revised), 2005.

First published 2009 by Folens Limited.

Every effort has been made to contact copyright holders of material used in this publication. If any copyright holder has been overlooked, we should be pleased to make any necessary arrangements.

British Library Cataloguing in Publication Data. A catalogue record for this publication is available from the British Library.

ISBN 978-1-85008-425-9   Folens code FD4259

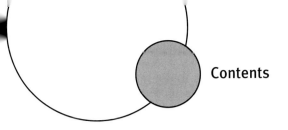

Contents

Contents list

Introduction to the Teacher Support Pack

Chapter One: Understanding Personal Development and Relationships [Edexcel Unit 1; OCR Unit A912]

Introduction

Additional resources for Chapter One on CD-ROM

All pages from Chapter One are available as pdfs and editable Word documents

1.1 'Growth and development' suggested answers ppt

1.2(E) 'Life stages for Edexcel' interactive

1.2(O) 'Life stages for OCR' interactive

1.3 'Advice on using centile charts' ppt

1.4 'Jessica' suggested answers ppt

1.5 'The nature versus nurture debate' suggested answers ppt

1.6 'Factors affecting growth and development' suggested answers ppt

1.7 'Definition of self-concept' ppt

1.8 'The effects of relationships and life events' suggested answers ppt

1.9 'Holmes-Rahe Adjustment Scale' ppt

'Understanding personal development and relationships revision quiz for Edexcel' interactive

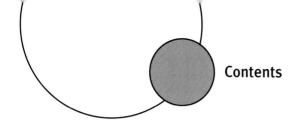

Contents

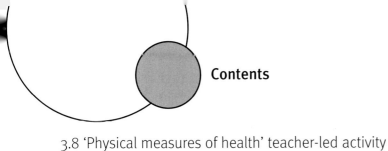

Contents

Additional resources for Chapter Three on CD-ROM

All pages from Chapter Three are available as pdfs and editable Word documents

3.1 'Definitions of health and well-being' ppt

3.1 'Definitions of health and well-being' interactive

3.2 'List of leaflet suppliers' pdf

3.2 'List of leaflet suppliers' Word document

3.3 'Designing a health questionnaire' ppt

3.4(O) 'Factors that contribute to positive health' suggested answers ppt

3.8A 'Organizing a physical assessment' film clip

3.8B 'Taking a blood pressure measurement' film clip

3.8C 'Taking a peak flow measurement' film clip

3.8D 'Assessing someone's height/weight/BMI' film clip

3.8E 'Taking a waist to hip ratio measurement' film clip

3.8F 'Resting pulse and recovery rate measurement' film clip

'Promoting health and well-being revision quiz' interactive

Chapter Four: Safeguarding and Protecting Individuals [OCR Unit A914]

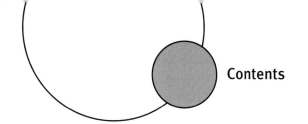

Contents

Additional resources for Chapter Four on CD-ROM

All pages from Chapter Four are available as pdfs and editable Word documents

4.1 'Safeguarding individuals' suggested answers on ppt

4.2 'Safeguarding individuals quiz' suggested answers on ppt

4.4 'A hand washing procedure' film clip

4.5A 'Putting someone in the recovery position' film clip

4.5B 'Abdominal thrusts' film clip

4.6 'First-aid wordsearch' answers on ppt

4.7 'Legislation' ppt

4.8 'Safety information signs' interactive

4.9 'What to do in the event of a fire' ppt

'Food hygiene' interactive

'First-aid quiz' interactive

'Mark scheme for Folens' Practice Test for OCR Unit A914' pdf

Chapter Five: Health, Social Care and Early Years in Practice [Edexcel Unit 4]

Additional resources for Chapter Five on CD-ROM

All pages from Chapter Five are available as pdfs and editable Word documents

5.1 'Care needs' suggested answers on ppt

5.4 'Care values' ppt

5.5 'Discrimination' suggested answers on ppt

5.7 'Self-concept' suggested answers on ppt

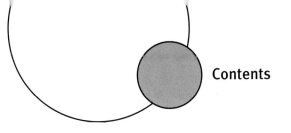

Contents

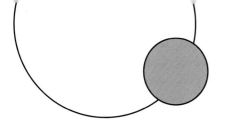

Introduction

Folens GCSE Health and Social Care Teacher's Support Pack is designed to be used with *Folens GCSE Health and Social Care Double Award Student Books* to make this challenging subject real, engaging and teachable.

This pack contains guidance for both Edexcel and OCR teachers. The detailed table of contents at the beginning of the chapters will let you know which part of the Edexcel or OCR specification each resource relates to. Most of the resources can be used for both specifications. Where a resource is designed specifically for the Edexcel or OCR specification only, this can be seen from the table, from the resource number (which will contain either an (E) or (O) suffix) and is signposted in the top right hand corner of the page. Chapter Four of the Teacher's Support Pack is for OCR only, covering OCR Unit A914, 'Safeguarding and protecting individuals'. Chapter Five of the Pack is for Edexcel only, covering Edexcel Unit 4, 'Health, Social Care and Early Years in Practice'.

The Pack consists of a photocopiable book and CD-ROM. All the pages of the book are available as pdfs on the CD-ROM for you to print out. All the worksheets, case studies and information sheets are also available as editable Word documents, so that you can personalize the material for your students. The CD-ROM also contains additional pdfs, PowerPoints®, film clips and interactives to support the worksheets and activities in the book. The table of contents for each chapter will detail how you can best use these components together.

The Pack consists of the following elements:

- **'Introducing this chapter'** contains guidance on specification content and assessment for each board, and some additional tips on teaching the unit. There is a detailed table of contents for each chapter, showing exactly which strand of the specification each resource covers, and the additional resources available to support the activity.
- **Editable worksheets** for students to do in class or for homework.
- **Teacher-led activities** for whole class participation, addressing different learning styles.
- **Information sheets and case studies** to support the worksheets and activities.
- **Editable PowerPoints®** for use in the classroom. Suggested answers for the worksheets are often included on PowerPoint® so that they can be discussed as a class.
- **Film clips** covering physical measures of health, and health and safety procedures. We realize how beneficial it is to invite practitioners into the classroom, and how difficult this can be to achieve practically.
- **Interactives**, including an animation of the life stages, key term and multiple choice revision quizzes.
- **Useful contacts and web addresses** and research activities, to take the subject beyond the four walls of the classroom.
- **Practice tests** for the externally assessed units for each board, with accompanying mark schemes. Please note these papers have not been through exam board quality assurance procedures.

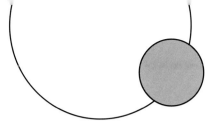

About the authors

Sue Morris is Principal Moderator for a major awarding body for GCSE and GCE Health and Social Care. She is also a practising Health Visitor for North Yorkshire & York Primary Care Trust.

Marion Tyler is an award-winning health professional specializing in stress management and complementary therapies. She has over 20 years' private and public sector experience training groups and individuals.

James O'Leary is Chief Examiner for the Diploma in Society, Health and Development Level 3 for a major awarding body. He is also an experienced writer, trainer and former teacher.

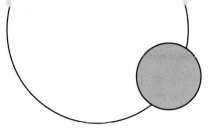

CHAPTER ONE: Understanding Personal Development and Relationships [Edexcel Unit 1; OCR Unit A912]

Introducing this chapter

'Understanding Personal Development and Relationships' is an externally tested unit and requires learners to draw on knowledge and understanding of human growth and development, factors affecting growth and development, the effects of relationships on growth and development and the effects of life events on development.

Edexcel Unit 1

The topics covered are:

1.1 Human growth and development
- The different life stages for Edexcel are:
  - infancy (0–2)
  - early childhood (3–8)
  - adolescence (9–18)
  - early adulthood (19–45)
  - middle adulthood (46–65)
  - later adulthood (65+)

1.2 Factors affecting human growth and development

1.3 Effects of relationships on personal growth and development

1.4 The effect of life events on personal development

Edexcel assessment

Assessment for this unit is through a 75-minute written examination with a total of 70 marks available. The paper is divided into two sections.
- Section 1: Fifteen multiple-choice questions with a total of 15 marks available.
- Section 2: A series of questions, requiring short to medium-length answers, based on case studies and short scenarios.
- All questions are compulsory. They will test knowledge and understanding, and the ability to apply that knowledge and understanding to a range of contexts. Students will need to analyse and evaluate issues and problems and draw reasoned conclusions from the material presented.
- The quality of written communication WILL be assessed throughout the written paper. Students will be guided via the rubrics of the paper as to which questions will be used to assess written communication. Examiners will be looking for evidence of accurate spelling, punctuation, grammar and clarity of expression.
- Papers should be accessible to all students with questions and mark schemes being tiered to allow the weaker candidates to access marks, even on the harder questions.

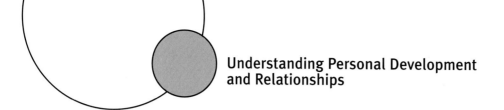

OCR Unit A912

The topics covered are:

3.2.1 The stages and patterns of human growth and development
- The different life stages for OCR are:
  - infancy (0–3)
  - childhood (4–10)
  - adolescence (11–18)
  - adulthood (19–65)
  - later adulthood (65+)

3.2.2 The different factors that can affect human growth and development

3.2.3 The development of self-concept and different types of relationships

3.2.4 Major life changes and sources of support

OCR assessment

Assessment for this unit is through a 1-hour written examination with a total of 60 marks available.

- The paper will consist of a series of questions, requiring short to medium-length answers, based on case studies and short scenarios.
- All questions are compulsory. They will test knowledge and understanding, and the ability to apply that knowledge and understanding to a range of contexts. Students will need to analyse and evaluate issues and problems, and draw reasoned conclusions from the material presented.
- The quality of written communication WILL be assessed throughout the written paper. Examiners will be looking for evidence of accurate spelling, punctuation, grammar and clarity of expression. Writing should be legible and meaning should be clear.
- Papers should be accessible to all students with questions and mark schemes being tiered to allow the weaker candidates to access marks even on the harder questions.

Notes on using this chapter

In this chapter, we introduce the students to Andy and his family. Several worksheets are based around case studies on this imaginary family. You may wish to photocopy and laminate the case studies, or provide each student with their own copy.

There are two practice exam papers included at the end of the section. The format of these is different depending on whether you are teaching the Edexcel qualification or the OCR qualification. The mark schemes for both papers can be found on the accompanying CD-ROM. **Please note, neither of these papers has been through the strict quality assurance procedures laid down by both Edexcel and OCR and, therefore, cannot be guaranteed to be an accurate reflection of the actual exam.**

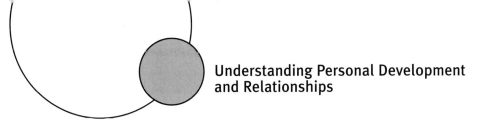

Table of contents for this chapter

     GCSE Health & Social Care   © Folens (copiable page)

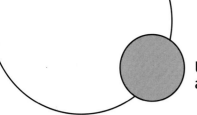
17		'Andy's family' case study	1.2, 1.3, 1.4	3.2.2, 3.2.4	
20	1.7	'The development of self-concept' worksheet	1.2, 1.3, 1.4	3.2.2, 3.2.3, 3.2.4	1. 'Andy's family' case study (p17) 2. 'Definition of self-concept' ppt 1.7 (CD-ROM)
21	1.8	'The effects of relationships and life events' teacher-led activity	1.3, 1.4	3.2.3, 3.2.4	1. 'Andy's family' case study (p17) 2. Suggested answers on ppt 1.8 (CD-ROM)
22	1.9	'Life events' worksheet	1.4	3.2.4	1. 'Andy's family' case study (p17) 2. 'Holmes-Rahe Adjustment Scale' ppt 1.9 (CD-ROM)
23	1.10	'Life changes' worksheet	1.4	3.2.4	'Andy's family' case study (p17)
24		Folens' Practice Test for Edexcel	Unit 1		1. Mark scheme pdf (CD-ROM) 2. 'Revision quiz for Edexcel' interactive (CD-ROM)
36		Folens' Practice Test for OCR		Unit A912	1. Mark scheme pdf (CD-ROM) 2. 'Revision quiz for OCR' interactive (CD-ROM)

GCSE Health & Social Care

Growth and development

Using the words in the box below, complete the paragraph underneath to give definitions of the words 'growth', 'development' and 'norm'.

complexity	head circumference	weight
milestones	size	emotional
maturity	skills	physical

Growth is an increase in physical _____. It is determined by measuring height,

_____ and, in small babies, _____ .

Development is an increase in c_____ . It is concerned with the emergence

and increase in sophistication of s_____ . It is a continuous process from conception

through to m_____ . Development is usually considered across four areas. These are

_____ , intellectual, _____ and social.

A **norm** is a fixed or ideal standard. Developmental norms are sometimes called

_____ . These denote markers in the recognized pattern of physical development. An

example of a milestone would be that a baby should be able to sit, without support, by the

age of nine months.

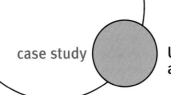

Introducing Andy and his family

Andy, Kerry and their daughter, Jessica, live together in a small house near Leeds in West Yorkshire. Andy is 24 years of age. He works as a bricklayer and is a fitness fanatic. Kerry is 23 years of age. She has a part-time job in a local dress shop. Jessica is just 2 years of age. She was born with a condition called cerebral palsy.

Christine is Andy's mother and Jessica's grandmother. She lives a few miles away in the next town. Christine is 52 years of age. Christine's first husband, Andy's father, died several years ago after suffering from lung cancer.

Christine has recently met, and married, Ian, who is 65 and works as a volunteer at a hospice. They live with Christine's son, Paul, who is Andy's brother. He is still at school studying for his A levels. He is hoping to go to university to study Law when he leaves school.

Life stages

There are **six** life stages in the human life span and each has specific characteristics that identify it from another. Using the case study 'Introducing Andy and his family', complete the table below. Identify the life stage for each character. Then, for each life stage, identify **one** key feature of each area of development.

Character	Life stage and age range	Key feature of physical development	Key feature of intellectual development	Key feature of emotional development	Key feature of social development
Jessica					
Paul					
Andy					
Kerry					
Christine					
Ian					

Life stages

There are **five** life stages in the human life span and each has specific characteristics that identify it from another. Using the case study 'Introducing Andy and his family', complete the table below. Identify the life stage for each character. Then, for each life stage, identify **one** key feature of each area of development.

Character	Life stage and age range	Key feature of physical development	Key feature of intellectual development	Key feature of emotional development	Key feature of social development
Jessica					
Paul					
Andy					
Kerry					
Christine					
Ian					

GCSE Health & Social Care © Folens (copiable page)

Jessica

Jessica has cerebral palsy, a condition usually caused by damage to the developing brain in the later months of pregnancy, during birth or in the first few weeks of life. The injury damages the brain's ability to control the muscles.

Jessica spent the first eight weeks of her life in the Special Care Baby Unit at the local hospital. Andy and Kerry visited her every day but it was not the same as having their baby at home with them. Because of her condition, Jessica did not grow at the normal rate and is still smaller than average for a child of her age.

Jessica's muscles are very stiff and she has great difficulty walking. She visits the local hospital regularly for intensive physiotherapy to try and aid her walking. The physiotherapists have provided her with a special walking frame to help her get around.

Cerebral palsy has also affected Jessica's ability to speak as she has little control over the muscles in her mouth. As a result of her condition, Jessica's verbal and motor skills are developing at a very slow rate. She understands everything that her parents say to her but she is unable to express herself.

Kerry and Jessica receive a great deal of support from the Portage service provided by the local authority and also from SCOPE, a charity set up specifically to provide support to people with cerebral palsy. Portage is a home-based early educational intervention service provided specifically for children with particular educational needs. The Portage worker, Jenny, has taught Kerry and Jessica to use Makaton, a type of sign language that means that Jessica can communicate and sign her needs.

Jessica attends Rainbow Day Nursery when Kerry is at work. Kuldeep, the nursery nurse in Jessica's class, has also learnt Makaton and is working closely with Jessica to develop her skills. Kuldeep, Kerry and Jenny meet together regularly to discuss a plan of action for Jessica in order to ensure that activities are provided that will encourage her development.

Using centile charts

To monitor the normal pattern of growth or any deviations from it, health professionals use centile charts to plot a range of measurements including weight, height and head circumference. A normal pattern of growth would show these three measurements following the same pattern and in proportion with each other.

You will find two centile charts, one for length and weight for age and one for head circumference compared to weight, on the next two sheets. You will need to photocopy them both for each student. You will also need to explain to the students how centile charts are used. Information can be found on **PowerPoint® 1.3** on the CD-ROM.

The aims of this activity are to introduce students to centile charts, and to enable them to identify both a normal pattern of growth and one that deviates away from the norm. By the end, it should also enable students to use centile charts to predict growth.

Resources
- The case study, 'Jessica'. Students have already been introduced to the character 'Jessica' but this case study will give them more background information.
- One copy of the 'Growth measurements' information sheet per person or per group.
- One copy of both charts on the 'Centile charts' information sheet.
- PowerPoint® 1.3 on using centile charts.
- Red and blue pens.

Instructions
1. Using the measurements given for Katie, which can be found on the 'Growth measurements' information sheet, ask the students to plot these on their charts using a blue pen. (All measurements provided are metric.)

NB. The plotted points on a centile chart SHOULD NOT be joined up. This is not a graph.

2. Now ask the students to plot the measurements for Jessica, also on the 'Growth measurements' information sheet, on the same charts using a red pen.

3. In groups, ask the students to draw conclusions about:
   a) Katie's measurements
   b) Jessica's measurements.

4. Ask the question: 'If Katie was to continue following a normal pattern of growth what would her weight and length be when she reaches 2 years of age (24 months)?'

5. Ask the question: 'When Jessica was 14 months old, she contracted measles and was ill for several weeks. As a result, she lost weight. She dropped from the 25th centile down to the 5th centile by the time she was 16 months of age. What was her weight when she was 16 months old?'

Plenary
Bring the groups together and discuss the two charts, drawing conclusions about the two girls' growth.

Growth measurements

Katie

Below you will find a table showing measurements, from birth, for Katie, who is 13 months of age. All measurements are metric.

Age in months	Weight in kilograms	Length in centimetres	Head circumference in centimetres
Birth	3.4	50.1	34.8
2 months	5.2	56.5	38.8
5 months	6.8	63.8	42.0
9 months	8.6	68.5	44.0
12 months	9.4	78	45.0

Jessica

Below you will find a table showing measurements from birth to 12 months of age for Jessica, who is now two years old. All measurements are metric.

Age in months	Weight in kilograms	Length in centimetres	Head circumference in centimetres
Birth	2.4	48.0	33.8
2 months	3.8	55.0	38.0
5 months	5.8	61.0	41.0
9 months	7.4	67.0	43.0
12 months	8.6	70.0	44.2

GCSE Health & Social Care

© Folens (copiable page)

Centile charts

Girls' growth chart – Length and weight

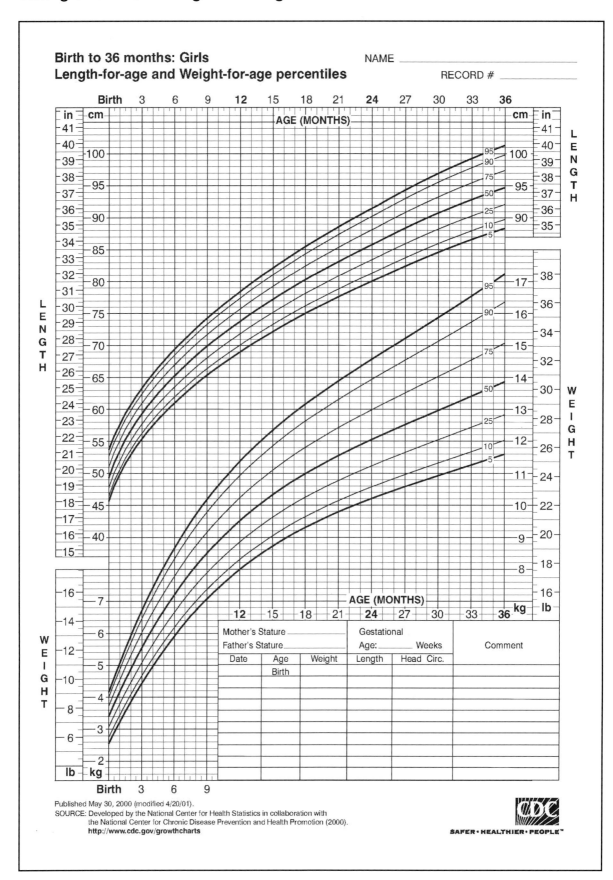

Girls' growth chart – Head circumference and weight

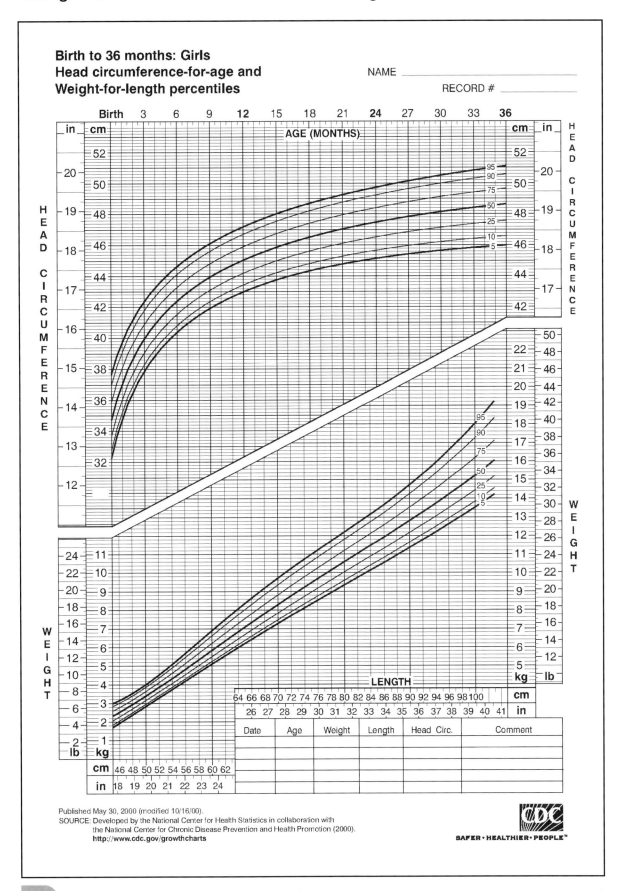

Birth to 36 months: Girls
Head circumference-for-age and
Weight-for-length percentiles

NAME _____

RECORD # _____

Published May 30, 2000 (modified 10/16/00).
SOURCE: Developed by the National Center for Health Statistics in collaboration with
the National Center for Chronic Disease Prevention and Health Promotion (2000).
http://www.cdc.gov/growthcharts

Jessica

1. Jessica is two years of age. Below you will find a list of skills that Jessica **should** have mastered by the age of two years. Complete the table, stating whether they represent physical, intellectual, emotional or social development.

2. For the skills you identify as 'physical development', state whether they are gross motor or fine motor skills.

Skill	Area of development
Climbs onto furniture	
Uses approximately 50 words	
Is able to hold a pencil and scribble	
Engages in pretend play	
Develops a sense of identity, for example, 'I am me'	
Runs safely	
May be able to dress but struggles with buttons	
Uses a pincer grasp to pick up objects	
Enjoys looking at books and pretending to read	
Engages in parallel play, for example, playing alongside another child, not with them	

3. Jessica has cerebral palsy. Look back at the case study 'Jessica' to ensure you understand the effects this has had on her development.

   a) Which life stage is Jessica currently in?

   ....

   b) Using the case study, identify which two areas of Jessica's development are most affected.

   (i) .... (ii) ....

The nature versus nurture debate

A question that many people ask is 'To what extent is our development affected by our genes or the environment in which we live?' This is the 'nature versus nurture debate'.

1. Identify which of the following factors are influenced by our genes (nature) and which are influenced by our environment (nurture).

Factor	Nature or nurture?
Jamelia has dark brown eyes	
Martha is very quiet when in a group	
Catherine is an Olympic swimmer and won a gold medal	
Mrs Smith has a BMI of 32.4	
Mark is 1.88 metres tall	
Jayden did not learn to walk until he was 22 months old	
Christopher is only 7 years of age but has a reading age of 11	
Peter is very disruptive in class. He has a condition known as Attention Deficit Hyperactivity Disorder	
Mr Patel is suffering from lung cancer	
Mrs King has breast cancer	

2. Compare your completed table with a friend's table.

   a) Do you disagree about any of the factors?

   b) Are there any factors for which you were unable to decide which category to put them in?

   c) Make notes about why it was difficult for you to decide.

   Suggested answers can be found on **PowerPoint® 1.5**.

Extension activity

You may now be able to see how difficult it is to decide whether our development is affected by our environment or our genes. Researchers will often try to answer this question by undertaking studies using identical twins, that is, twins who have **exactly** the same genetic make-up.

Using the information from the activity above, write a short paragraph explaining why you think it is important that **identical twins** are used for this type of research.

Factors affecting growth and development

A variety of factors may affect the way humans grow and develop. Some of these are within our control and others are not. These factors may have a positive or a negative effect on our personal development, and our health and well-being.

Complete the table below by stating whether the situation is as a result of **physical**, **social**, **cultural**, **emotional**, **economic** or **psychological** factors, or as a result of the **physical environment**. Some situations may be a result of more than one factor. You might need to do some research to complete the last column. Some boxes have been completed for you.

Situation	Control or no control	Type of factor	Possible effect on growth and development
Dev goes to the gym three times a week	Control	Physical	Regular exercise reduces the risk of heart disease. May make friends so improves social development.
Mr Macheta is homeless and sleeps rough in the centre of a large city			
Aaron was born with cystic fibrosis, a genetic disorder			Failure to grow within normal limits due to malabsorption of nutrients. Recurrent chest infections may mean time missed from school, which might affect intellectual development.
Paul has just lost his job		Economic	
Suneeta tries to eat five portions of fruit and vegetables every day			
The Smith family have just moved to a new house and do not know anyone in the area			
Tom regularly drinks ten pints of beer on a Friday night	Control		
Andy and Kerry are getting divorced			Both are more likely to suffer from anxiety and depression. One or both may lose their home. Financially worse off, so standard of living may be affected, which can affect diet. Socially, one or both may lose friends.

Andy's family

Jessica

Jessica is two years of age. She suffers from cerebral palsy, a condition that affects her muscles, resulting in a delay in her physical and language development. Following her birth, Jessica was very ill and spent the first eight weeks of her life in a Special Care Baby Unit. Kerry and Andy, Jessica's parents, were only able to visit Jessica for one hour a day and, for the first two months, could not take Jessica out of the incubator (a special cot that ensures babies are kept at the right temperature and keeps them free from possible infection). This meant that Kerry and Andy were unable to cuddle Jessica, and Kerry was unable to breast feed her. This upset Kerry very much. Jessica receives a great deal of help from physiotherapists, a Portage service and also from the staff at the day nursery she attends.

Recently, Andy had an accident and spent several weeks in hospital. Jessica was unable to see him regularly. Now Andy and Kerry are getting divorced and Kerry is moving to live in a different part of the country with Jessica. This means she will not see her dad very often.

Paul

Paul is 17 years of age and is currently studying at school for his A levels. His predicted grades are very good and he is hoping to get a place at Manchester University to study Law. Paul has lots of friends at school and is the captain of the school football team.

Several months ago, Paul met Abi and they are now in a serious and intimate relationship. Abi does not want to go to university and Paul is a little worried about what might happen to their relationship when he leaves home.

Paul has an excellent relationship with his brother, Andy, and was very upset about Andy's accident. He looks on Andy as a substitute father, as Andy took responsibility for Paul's upbringing after their father died. However, Paul and Christine, his mum, argue constantly. Paul is not happy about the fact that Ian has now moved in to live with him and his mum, and he does not have a good relationship with Ian. Paul cannot wait to leave home. He is looking forward to going to university.

GCSE **Health & Social Care** © Folens (copiable page)

Andy

Andy is 24 years of age. When he was 14 years of age his father died. He was very upset and, as a result, stopped working hard at school and failed all his GCSEs. He left school with no qualifications but managed to get a job as a trainee bricklayer. A few months ago, he completed a course with the Open University, gaining a 'Distinction'. Andy married Kerry when he was 21 and, one year later, their daughter, Jessica, was born. Andy was delighted that he had a daughter but devastated when he realized she would always be disabled.

A few weeks ago, while working high up on a building site, Andy slipped and fell from the scaffolding, landing on his head and sustaining severe head injuries. Andy suffered a type of stroke; the part of his brain that sends messages to move his limbs no longer functions properly. Andy has been told he will have to spend several months in hospital and will never walk again. Kerry and Jessica visited regularly, at first, but as the weeks have gone on, they have visited the hospital less and less. Kerry has just asked Andy for a divorce.

Andy has had great difficulty in accepting his situation. He was a cheerful, happy-go-lucky person who had lots of friends and went out regularly, but now he doesn't want to see anyone. He is self-conscious about the way he looks and the fact that he is in a wheelchair. The doctors are pleased with Andy's progress; however, despite this, Andy feels useless and worthless.

Kerry

Kerry married Andy when she was just 20 years of age. They had known each other for several years and the day they got married was the happiest day of Kerry's life. She was ecstatic when she found out she was pregnant; however, all the way through the pregnancy she felt ill and the midwife was very concerned that the baby was not growing properly. When Kerry was 32 weeks pregnant, the doctor decided to induce her labour and her daughter, Jessica, was born. Jessica was very small and it was necessary to take her straight to the Special Care Baby Unit, where she stayed until she was eight weeks old. Kerry and Andy did not get to hold and cuddle her for several weeks after she was born. Kerry felt that she did not 'bond' with Jessica and, at first, resented the fact that her daughter had developmental problems.

Kerry received a lot of support from her health visitor and from SCOPE, the charitable organization set up to help people with cerebral palsy and their families. When Jessica was 18 months old, Kerry decided to go back to work part time. She loved her job and had several work friends that she went out with on a regular basis. Andy was happy to care for Jessica.

Following Andy's accident, Kerry became very depressed as she realized she would have to give up work to care for both Jessica and Andy. She felt she could no longer cope and asked Andy for a divorce.

Christine

Christine is 52 years of age and, following the death of her first husband several years ago, has devoted her life to working as a volunteer at the hospice where her husband died. She missed her husband greatly for some considerable time but, as the years went by and her family grew, firstly with Andy's marriage to Kerry and then the birth of her first grandchild, Jessica, she gradually came to terms with her loss. Andy was a great help to her in the early months and years, and helped her bring up her younger son, Paul.

About one year ago, Christine met Ian. Ian is slightly older than Christine and also works as a volunteer at the hospice. Ian and Christine decided to get married a few months ago. Andy was delighted but Paul, who still lives at home, was not happy about the new relationship. He felt that Ian was trying to take the place of his father and whenever Ian told Paul off for staying out late, for example, Paul would have an enormous argument with him and storm out of the house. This volatile relationship upsets Christine greatly and she often feels that her loyalties are split between her son, whom she loves dearly, and her new husband.

Ian

Ian is 65 years of age. He works as a volunteer at the local hospice and has done so since his daughter, who was 34, died of breast cancer four years ago. The hospice supported Ian so well both during his daughter's illness and after she had died that he wanted to give something back. It also gave him a focus, and allowed him to mix with other people and make new friends.

About one year ago, Ian met Christine who was also working as a volunteer at the hospice following the death of her husband. Ian found that he could talk to Christine easily and felt they shared a common bond. After a couple of months, Ian asked Christine out and, not long ago, Ian and Christine decided to get married. Both of them still work at the hospice and have met many good friends there.

Although Ian and Christine are very happy, Ian does not get on well with Christine's son, Paul. Paul is 17 and feels that Ian is trying to take the place of his father. Ian and Paul argue about almost everything and this is putting a strain on Ian's relationship with Christine. Ian feels that Christine always takes Paul's side in any argument and he often feels like an outsider in what is now his home. Ian is looking forward to the day when Paul goes to university and he can start his life with Christine properly.

The development of self-concept

Fill the gaps in the following sentences to provide you with a definition of self-concept.

Self-concept is a combination of s_____ - i_____ and s_____ -e_____,

which together produce a sense of personal i_____ . Self-image is the way we

s_____ ourselves.

Self-esteem is how we v _____ ourselves, our sense of worth.

Our self-concept can be affected by a number of factors. These are listed in the box below.

Age	Appearance	Gender	Culture
	Emotional development	Education	
	Relationships with others	Sexual orientation	

Using the case study, 'Andy's family', answer the following questions:

1. Name one factor from Andy's life so far that may be contributing to his self-concept in a positive way and one factor that may be contributing in a negative way.

   Positive ....

   Negative ....

2. Briefly explain why you think these factors may be having the effect they are on Andy's self-concept.

Extension activities

3. Now consider all the factors listed in the box above. Put the factors in order of how important you think they are for Andy's self-concept, starting with the most important.

4. Try to answer the above questions for the other members of Andy's family. Do you notice a difference depending on the age of the person? Discuss your findings with the rest of your class.

teacher
-led
activity

1.8

**Understanding Personal Development
and Relationships**

The effects of relationships and life events

The aim of this activity is to allow students to investigate the possible effects of relationships and life events on personal development. It should also allow them to explore the support networks available by considering the various individuals within the case study, 'Andy's family'.

Resources
- Copies of the character profiles from 'Andy's family'. (You may want to photocopy and laminate these for future use.)
- Paper and pens.

Instructions
1. Divide the class up into six groups.

2. Give each group one of the character profiles from the case study, 'Andy's family'.

3. Ask the groups to:

   a) identify the life stage of their given individual

   b) identify the factors that have affected the development of their individual in the past

   c) identify the factors that may be affecting development now

   d) identify the support networks that may be involved with their chosen individual and state whether they are informal carers, formal carers or community/voluntary services

   e) finally, discuss what they think might happen if that support was not available for their individual.

Plenary
Bring groups together to discuss their findings. Suggested answers can be found on **PowerPoint® 1.8**.

Extension activity
Interview two people who are over 65 years of age. Ask them to explain which have been their favourite and least favourite life stages, giving some reasons. Discuss the findings with other people in the class. Consider the following:

- Are there any differences between men and women?

- What factors do you think are most important in determining a person's favourite and least favourite life stages?

GCSE Health & Social Care © Folens (copiable page)

Life events

Expected and unexpected life events will affect our lives in all sorts of different ways. Our whole view on life may be changed or the life events may affect our daily living. What is guaranteed, however, is that life events, either good or bad, will be stressful.

Consider the information in the case study, 'Andy's family'. It refers to two life stages in Andy's life.

1. Name the two life stages.

   a) ....

   b) ....

2. Using the Holmes-Rahe Social Adjustment Scale, which can be found on **PowerPoint® 1.9**, work out which was the most stressful life stage for Andy by adding up the scores for the life events he experienced.

   A score of 150 or less means a relatively low (about 30 per cent) probability of suffering from a stress-related illness (including a heart attack, cancer, stroke, and so on). A score of 151 to 299 implies a 50 per cent probability of this and a score of 300 or above implies an 80 per cent probability of experiencing a health change – usually a negative change.

3. Using the information above, complete the final column of the table and draw some conclusions. Discuss your results with a partner. Did you draw the same conclusions about Andy's current and future health?

Life stage 1	Life events	Score	Conclusions
	Total		
Life stage 2	Life events	Score	Conclusions
	Total		

GCSE Health & Social Care   © Folens (copiable page)

Life changes

After reading through the character profiles on 'Andy's family', choose **two** examples of **unexpected life events** for Andy or one of his family. Complete the table below, identifying the possible effects on development that these events might have.

Unexpected life event	Effect on physical development	Effect on intellectual development	Effect on emotional development	Effect on social development

GCSE Health & Social Care © Folens (copiable page)

Folens' Practice Test for Edexcel

Time allowed: 1 hour 15 minutes

Instructions

- Use **BLACK** ink or ballpoint pen.

- Answer **ALL** the questions.

- Answer the questions in the space provided – there may be more space than you need.

Information

- The total mark for this paper is 70.

- The marks for **each** question are shown in brackets at the end of each question or part question – use this as a guide as to how much time to spend on each question.

- Questions marked with an **asterisk** (*) are ones where the quality of your written communication will be assessed. You should take particular care with your spelling, punctuation and grammar, as well as your clarity of expression, when answering these questions.

Advice

- Read each question carefully and make sure you know what you have to do before starting your answer.

- Keep an eye on the time.

- Try to answer every question.

- Check your answers if you have time at the end.

Section One

Answer ALL questions.

In Section One, questions must be answered with a cross in a box. ☒

If you change your mind, put a line through the box ☒ **and then indicate your new answer with a cross.** ☒

1. What is the age range for humans in the early childhood stage of life?

    ☐ **A**   0–4 years

    ☐ **B**   3–8 years

    ☐ **C**   0–2 years

    ☐ **D**   4–7 years   (1)

2. What is the name given to the developmental period when secondary sexual characteristics develop?

    ☐ **A**   Pubescence

    ☐ **B**   Adolescent

    ☐ **C**   Puberty

    ☐ **D**   Menopause   (1)

3. The way we feel about ourselves is known as our:

    ☐ **A**   Self-concept

    ☐ **B**   Self-awareness

    ☐ **C**   Self-image

    ☐ **D**   Self-esteem   (1)

GCSE Health & Social Care   © Folens (copiable page)

4. Which **two** of the following are characteristics of middle adulthood?

     A   Menstruation ceases

     B   Skin becomes wrinkled

     C   Facial hair grows

     D   Ovulation stops

☐ A and B

☐ A and D

☐ B and C

☐ B and D   (1)

5. Which **two** of the following are examples of fine motor skills?

     A   Running

     B   Colouring a picture

     C   Using a knife and fork

     D   Hopping

☐ A and B

☐ B and C

☐ B and D

☐ A and C   (1)

6. Which of the following is an economic factor that may affect development?

☐ **A**   Income

☐ **B**   Housing conditions

☐ **C**   Exercise

☐ **D**   Education   (1)

7. Developing a strong emotional link with parents or carers is known as:

☐ **A**   Attainment

☐ **B**   Attachment

☐ **C**   Bondage

☐ **D**   Affection   (1)

8. Which of the following is an 'expected' life event?

☐ **A** Losing your job

☐ **B** Getting divorced

☐ **C** Starting school

☐ **D** Having a car accident   (1)

9. Making friends is a feature of which area of development?

☐ **A** Physical development

☐ **B** Emotional development

☐ **C** Social development

☐ **D** Intellectual development   (1)

10. A 'sibling' would be which type of relation?

☐ **A** A brother or sister

☐ **B** A parent

☐ **C** A cousin

☐ **D** An aunt or uncle   (1)

11. Which **two** of the following would be 'informal carers'?

A A relative

B A district nurse

C A neighbour

D A childminder

☐ A and D

☐ B and C

☐ A and C

☐ C and D   (1)

GCSE Health & Social Care   © Folens (copiable page)

12. The process of becoming fully developed is known as:

☐ **A** Maturation

☐ **B** Socialization

☐ **C** Ageing

☐ **D** Matriculation (1)

13. A 'developmental norm', which a person should reach by a certain age, is known as a:

☐ **A** Life event

☐ **B** Milestone

☐ **C** Life stage

☐ **D** Millstone (1)

14. A 'peer group' refers to:

☐ **A** A family group

☐ **B** A friendship group

☐ **C** An intimate sexual relationship

☐ **D** A religious group (1)

15. Which of the following characteristics would be determined by our genes?

☐ **A** Eye colour

☐ **B** Weight

☐ **C** Occupation

☐ **D** Lifestyle (1)

TOTAL FOR SECTION ONE = 15 MARKS

Section Two

Answer ALL questions.

16. Read the following case study and answer ALL of the questions that follow.

> Mrs Patel is 34 years of age and lives with her husband and three children, Suneeta, aged 11, Jared, aged 5, and Binda, aged 11 months. The family have a limited income as Mr Patel cannot work due to ill-health. Mrs Patel has a part-time job working as a cleaner five evenings a week and Suneeta regularly looks after the younger children.
>
> Mr and Mrs Patel live in a small, two-bedroomed house. The bedrooms are damp and the central heating doesn't work. The only source of heating is a coal fire in the living room.
>
> Suneeta has just moved to the local secondary school. She is very bright and was regularly getting full marks for her homework; however, recently her work has deteriorated. She has not yet made many friends with the other girls in her class and some of them have called her a 'swot' because of her good marks.

a) (i) Which life stage is Suneeta in?

.... (1)

(ii) Which life stage is Mrs Patel in?

.... (1)

b) Give **two** examples of secondary sexual characteristics that develop during Suneeta's current life stage.

(i) ....

(ii) .... (2)

c) Identify **one** unexpected life event that Mr Patel has experienced to date and explain how it may have affected his development.

Identify ....

Explain ....

....

....

.... (3)

GCSE Health & Social Care © Folens (copiable page)

d) Identify and explain **one** environmental factor that may be affecting Binda's growth and development.

....

....

....

....

....

....

....

(4)

e) Suneeta has a negative self-concept. Explain the possible effects this may have on her development.

....

....

....

....

....

....

....

....

....

....

(6)

f) *Discuss how Suneeta's development may be affected by her current situation.

....

....

....

....

....

....

....

....

....

....

....

....

....

....

....

....

....

....   (8)

Total for Question 16 = 25 marks

GCSE Health & Social Care © Folens (copiable page)

17. Read the following case study and answer ALL of the questions that follow.

> Bill is 76 years of age. His wife, Martha, died six months ago and since then Bill has lived on his own. He does not go out very much and has no friends. His daughter, June, is very worried about him as he is not eating properly.
>
> Bill recently spent several weeks in hospital after falling and breaking his leg. He is now at home and a district nurse visits daily to give Bill his medication. His daughter, June, works full time. She calls in every morning before going to work to help her father get washed and dressed. The Local Authority provide a 'Meals on wheels' service during the week and June has arranged for Bill's neighbour to pop in on a daily basis to make sure he is alright.
>
> June has also arranged for Bill to attend a day centre run by 'Help the Aged' once a week. This gets him out of the house and is allowing him to meet new people. He has also started playing chess with another man who attends the day centre.

a) Identify which life stage Bill is currently in.

....

.... (1)

b) Identify **two** physical changes that Bill may have experienced in this life stage.

....

....

....

.... (2)

c) Define what is meant by 'self-esteem'.

....

.... (1)

d) Explain why Bill might have a low self-esteem at the moment.

....

....

....

.... (2)

e) Identify and explain the importance of **two** different types of support that Bill is receiving to aid his recovery.

Identification 1 ....

Explanation ....

....

....

....

....

Identification 2 ....

Explanation ....

....

....

....

....

.... (6)

f) *Discuss the effect that Bill's accident may have had on his development.

....

....

....

....

....

....

....

....

....

....

....

....

....

....

.... (8)

GCSE Health & Social Care   © Folens (copiable page)

g) *Evaluate the effect that meeting people at the day centre might have on Bill's development.

....

....

....

....

....

....

....

....

....

....

....

....

....

....

....

....

.... (10)

Total for Question 17 = 30 marks

TOTAL FOR SECTION TWO = 55 MARKS

TOTAL FOR PAPER = 70 MARKS

GCSE **Health & Social Care** © Folens (copiable page)

Folens' Practice Test for OCR

Time allowed: 1 hour

Instructions

- Use **BLACK** ink or ballpoint pen.

- Answer **ALL** the questions.

- Answer the questions in the space provided – there may be more space than you need.

Information

- The total mark for this paper is 60.

- The marks for **each** question are shown in brackets at the end of each question or part question – use this as a guide as to how much time to spend on each question.

Advice

- Read each question carefully and make sure you know what you have to do before starting your answer.

- Keep an eye on the time.

- Try to answer every question.

- Check your answers if you have time at the end.

Answer ALL questions.

1. The Patel family consists of:

   • Misha, 34 years of age, works part time as a cleaner

   • Mr Patel, 72 years of age, Misha's father-in-law

   • Suneeta, 11 years of age, Misha's eldest daughter

   • Jared, 5 years of age, Misha's son

   • Binda, 11 months old, Misha's youngest daughter.

   a) Complete the following table to show the life stage and age range for that stage for each member of the Patel family.

The Patel family	Life stage	Age range
Misha, 34 years of age	Adulthood	
Mr Patel, 72 years of age		65+ years
Suneeta, 11 years of age		11–18 years
Jared, 5 years of age	Childhood	
Binda, 11 months old		

   (6)

   b) Identify **two** fine motor skills that a five-year-old child, who develops at the normal rate, could have achieved.

   1. ....

   2. ....   (2)

   c) Define what is meant by the term 'development'.

   ....

   ....

   ....

   ....   (2)

GCSE Health & Social Care   © Folens (copiable page)

d) Binda's weight and height are both following the 25th percentile on her growth chart.

Explain what this means in terms of her growth.

....

....

....

....

....

....

....

....

....

.... (5)

Total for Question 1 = 15 marks

GCSE Health & Social Care © Folens (copiable page)

2. Peter is 54 years of age. He lives on the outskirts of a small town on a very busy road. Peter works at a large chemical plant a few miles from his house and often has to work overtime at the plant to supplement his income. He has very little free time and, when he does have some time off work, he is usually so tired that he rarely goes out. As a result, he has very few friends.

a) Complete the table below, stating whether the examples listed are physical, social, environmental or economic factors affecting Peter's development. The first one has been completed for you.

Example	Factor
Peter lives on a busy road	Environmental
He works overtime to supplement his income	
He lives near a large chemical plant	
He has very little free time	
He has very few friends	
He is usually very tired	

(5)

b) Identify **two** sources of environmental pollution that affect Peter as a result of where he lives.

Source 1 ....

Source 2 ....

(2)

GCSE **Health & Social Care**

© Folens (copiable page)

c) Analyse how these two factors may affect Peter's development.

....

....

....

....

....

....

....

....

....

....

....

....

....

....

....   (8)

Total for Question 2 = 15 marks

GCSE Health & Social Care

© Folens (copiable page)

3. Simone is 15 years of age.

a) Which life stage is Simone currently in?

.... (1)

b) Identify **two** physical changes and **two** emotional changes that Simone is likely to experience in this life stage.

Physical	Emotional

(4)

c) Simone and her boyfriend, Charlie, have been together for several months. Charlie is three years older than Simone and would like to have a more serious relationship with her. Simone is doing well at school and is hoping to go to college after taking her GCSEs.

Discuss how Simone's relationship with Charlie may affect her development.

....

....

....

....

....

....

....

....

....

....

....

....

....

GCSE **Health & Social Care** © Folens (copiable page)

....

....

....

....

....

....

....

....

....

....

....

....

.... (10)

Total for Question 3 = 15 marks

4. Jayden is nine months of age. Below you will find a list of some of the milestones Jayden has reached.

a) Complete the table to show which area of development, physical, intellectual, language, emotional or social, each milestone represents. The first one has been completed for you.

Milestone	Area of development
Can sit unsupported	Physical
Babbles loudly	
Plays 'peek-a-boo'	
Transfers toys from one hand to the other	
Knows an object exists, even when it is out of sight	
Wary of strangers	

(5)

b) Lucy, Jayden's mum, divorced her husband a few months ago and moved to a new town.

From the information given in a) and b), state one **expected** life event and one **unexpected** life event.

Expected ....

Unexpected .... (2)

c) Jayden has an older sister, Melissa. She is five years of age and has just started at a new local primary school. Over the past few months, Melissa's behaviour at home has deteriorated and Lucy doesn't know how to handle her.

Identify **two** life events that may explain Melissa's behaviour.

Life event 1 ....

Life event 2 .... (2)

GCSE Health & Social Care © Folens (copiable page)

d) Explain how these life events are likely to affect Melissa's development.

....

....

....

....

....

....

....

....

....

....

....

.... (6)

Total for Question 4 = 15 marks

TOTAL FOR PAPER = 60 MARKS

GCSE Health & Social Care   © Folens (copiable page)

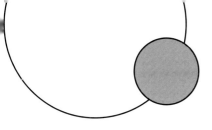

CHAPTER TWO: Health, Social Care and Early Years Provision

[Edexcel Unit 2: Exploring Health, Social Care and Early Years Provision; OCR Unit A911: Health, Social Care and Early Years Provision]

Introducing this chapter

'Health, Social Care and Early Years Provision' is an internally assessed unit in which students will benefit from access to work experience, visits to observe care workers in practice and visiting occupational speakers. Students will need to demonstrate the ability to apply knowledge and understanding of the needs of major client groups, access to and barriers to accessing services, types of services and how they are provided, the types of people, work roles and skills required in these services, and the values/principles that underpin them. Students will also be expected to analyse and evaluate information, draw conclusions and present reasoned judgements from the research undertaken.

Edexcel Unit 2: Exploring Health, Social Care and Early Years Provision

The topics covered are:

2.1 The range of care needs of major client groups

2.2 How health care, social care and early years services are accessed and the barriers to access

2.3 How health, social care and early years services are provided

2.4 Workers in health, social care and early years

2.5 Care values which underpin service provider interaction

Edexcel assessment

This unit is internally assessed and externally moderated. Students will produce a report that will be based on an investigation of the needs of one service user and how these needs are met by service providers and care practitioners.

Students will be expected to provide evidence from one of the following areas:

- health
- early years
- care of older people
- individuals with specific needs.

In carrying out the task, students will demonstrate their learning by applying their knowledge and understanding of the needs of one service user in their investigation. In addition, they will be expected to analyse and evaluate information, draw conclusions and present reasoned judgements from the research that they do. The quality of written communication will be assessed in this unit.

GCSE Health & Social Care © Folens (copiable page)

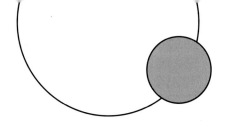

OCR Unit A911: Health, Social Care and Early Years Provision

The topics covered are:

3.1.1 The range of care needs of major client groups

3.1.2 The ways people can obtain services and the possible barriers that could prevent people from gaining access to services

3.1.3 The types of services that exist to meet client group needs and how they are developed and organized

3.1.4 The principles of care that underpin all care work with clients

3.1.5 The main work roles and skills of people who provide health, social care and early years services

OCR assessment

This unit is internally assessed and externally moderated. For OCR there will be a controlled assignment which will be re-issued every two years.

Students will be expected to provide evidence from one of the following areas:
- health
- early years
- care of older people
- individuals with specific needs.

In carrying out the task, students will demonstrate their learning by applying their knowledge and understanding of the needs of one service user in their investigation. In addition, they will be expected to analyse and evaluate information, draw conclusions and present reasoned judgements from the research that they do. The quality of written communication will be assessed in this unit.

GCSE Health & Social Care © Folens (copiable page)

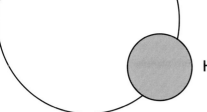

Table of contents for this chapter

Page	Resource no.	Resource title	Edexcel unit covered	OCR unit covered	Support resource
45		Introduction	Unit 2	Unit A911	
48	2.1	'Who uses health and social care services?' worksheet	2.1	3.1.1	
49	2.2	'How services meet individual needs' worksheet	2.1 & 2.3	3.1.1, 3.1.3	
50	2.3	'Who provides health and social care services?' worksheet	2.2	3.1.3	Suggested answers on ppt 2.3 (CD-ROM)
51	2.4	'Research' worksheet	Unit 2	Unit A911	'Definition of primary and secondary research' ppt 2.4 (CD-ROM)
52	2.5	'Who provides health and social care in your local area?' teacher-led activity	2.2	3.1.3	
53	2.6	'Methods of referral' worksheet	2.3	3.1.2	Suggested answers on ppt 2.6 (CD-ROM)
54	2.7	'Barriers to access' teacher-led activity	2.3	3.1.2	1. 'Barriers to access' ppt 2.7 (CD-ROM) 2. 'Barriers to access' interactive 2.7 (CD-ROM)
55	2.8	'Care values' worksheet	2.5	3.1.4	Suggested answers on ppt 2.8 (CD-ROM)
56	2.9	'Careers fair' teacher-led activity	2.4	3.1.5	
57	2.10	'A day in the life of ...' worksheet	2.4 & 2.5	3.1.4, 3.1.5	
			Unit 2	Unit A911	'Key terms revision' interactive (CD-ROM)

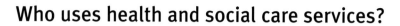

Who uses health and social care services?

Fill in the table below. In the first column, identify the life stage of the person pictured and then fill in the rest of the table to identify the types of services they might use. The first line has been filled in to start you off.

Life stage	One example of a service they might need	Who provides the service?	How can this service be accessed?
Adolescence Kayleigh (17 years of age)	Contraception advice	Local sexual health clinic	Drop-in session at the clinic
Jason (18 months old)			
Daniel (71 years of age)			
Priyanka (29 years of age)			

How services meet individual needs

This worksheet requires you to do some **primary research** in the form of an interview with an individual.

Ask your interviewee to think about a time they have used a health, social care or early years service. Did it meet their needs? Use the information gathered from your interview to fill in the table below. Remember, your interviewee may not understand what 'physical, intellectual, emotional and social needs' are, so you may need to explain these carefully to get the information that you need. You may find that the individual's needs were not adequately met.

Name of interviewee:

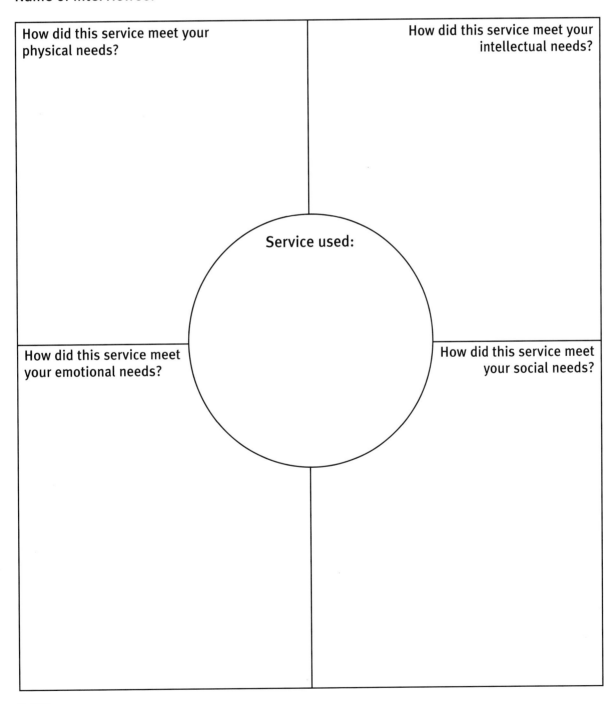

How did this service meet your physical needs?

How did this service meet your intellectual needs?

Service used:

How did this service meet your emotional needs?

How did this service meet your social needs?

GCSE Health & Social Care © Folens (copiable page)

Who provides health and social care services?

Complete the spider diagram showing six types of people or organizations who provide health services.

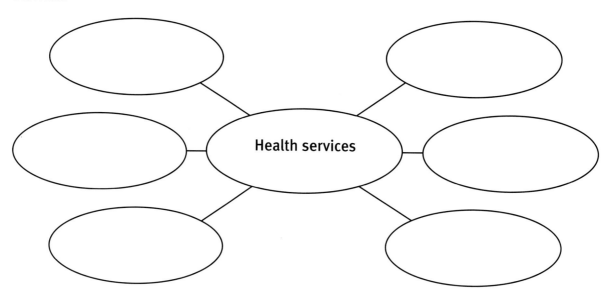

Now complete the spider diagram showing six types of people or organizations who provide social care services.

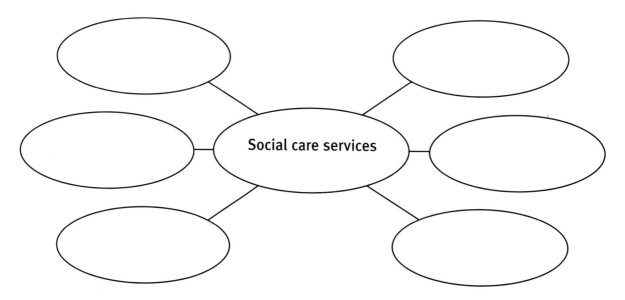

What do you understand is the difference between health services and social care services? Write down three things that are different:

1.

2.

3.

GCSE Health & Social Care © Folens (copiable page)

Research

To gather evidence for a report you will need to use **primary** and **secondary research**. Do you know what the difference is? Write a sentence or two to explain what each means.

```
Primary research
```

```
Secondary research
```

For your own report, keep a record of the research that you do in the following table:

Source	Type of information	Primary or secondary research?
For example, interview with a nursery nurse	*For example, description of their job role, skills and day-to-day tasks*	*For example, Primary*

Who provides health and social care services in your local area?

This activity asks students to identify the sorts of organizations and agencies that provide health and social care services in their local area.

Resources

- Access to the Internet for research purposes.
- Paper, pens, glue and other material for making posters.

Instructions

1. As a whole group, ask students to consider and discuss ways that they can find out information about who provides health and social care services in their local area. You might suggest Internet research, or collecting leaflets from local health centres, and local council offices or by going to the local library and using their information services.

2. Now split the class into small groups. Ask different groups to research and collect information on health care services, social care services and voluntary services in the area. You may need to set this as a homework task.

3. Ask students to present their research, either in a short presentation or by designing a poster. In particular, ask them to consider the demographic factors in your area that might have led to a particular service being introduced.

Extension activity

As a follow up, ask students to collect information about service provision in another area. Students should make comparisons and evaluate their findings. This could lead into a discussion about the idea of a 'postcode lottery'.

Methods of referral

There are three different methods of referral, listed below. Write a sentence or two to explain what each means.

Self-referral

Professional referral

Third-party referral

Can you identify the method of referral in the following scenarios? Fill in the table below.

Scenario	Method of referral
A customer collapses in the shop where Geeta works. She immediately calls the emergency services.	
Paul has a very high temperature and sore throat. He visits his GP.	
Kate has been feeling out of breath. After an initial examination, her GP arranges for her to have a chest X-ray.	
Cathy is concerned about her daughter's best friend after overhearing a conversation between the two of them. She telephones social services.	
Saskia has been experiencing severe headaches. She makes an appointment to have her eyes tested at the optician.	

Barriers to access

Asking students to role-play scenarios can give them a chance to empathize, as well as providing an opportunity for active learning. Here students are asked to consider the barriers that might prevent individuals from accessing the services they require.

Resources

- PowerPoint® 2.7, which shows the different types of barriers to access.

Instructions

1. To introduce the topic you could show **PowerPoint® 2.7**, which shows the different types of barriers that exist. You could start with a general discussion, asking students to give examples for each type of barrier and asking them to consider why it is important that care practitioners should be aware of these barriers.

2. Ask students to pair up. Within their pairs, ask students to pick one type of barrier, for example, physical barriers or language barriers. Ask each pair to make up a scenario showing an individual who has experienced a barrier to access. You could encourage students to draw on their own experiences, or those of someone they know, where they have encountered a barrier in real life. Explain that students will present their scenario to the rest of the class in interview format, with one student role-playing the individual and the other student role-playing an interviewer. Ask each pair to think about:

   a) the scenario in which a barrier was encountered

   b) how this made the individual feel

   c) a solution to overcoming the barrier

   d) how overcoming the barrier could make the individual feel.

3. Now ask for a pair to volunteer to present their scenario to the rest of the class. Students should use the interview format to describe the imaginary scenario and how this situation made the affected person feel.

4. The teacher should then ask the rest of the class to identify the type of barrier described in the scenario. The teacher should also ask the rest of the class to suggest ways in which the barrier could be overcome.

5. After hearing suggestions from the class, the pair should resume their presentation. The interviewer should describe their solution for overcoming the barrier, and the student playing the affected person should describe how this made them feel.

6. Repeat the presentation with some different volunteers from the class.

Care values

Write a set of care values that you would want an organization to apply if they were providing a service for the following people:

Anthony, a 14-year-old boy with a learning difficulty.

Dorothy, an 85-year-old Jewish woman living alone, with no family living close by.

Ravi, a 50-year-old man who has just lost his job.

Now choose your own care setting and list the care values that are applied in that setting:

Care setting:

Care values:

Careers fair

This activity asks students to investigate the qualities and qualifications of people who work in health and social care.

Resources

- Access to books and Internet resources, or to practitioners.
- Paper, pens, magazines and so on for making a poster.

Instructions

1. Explain to students that they are going to run a careers fair. Ask each student to design a poster showing the typical profile of either a direct or indirect carer. Information about the job role can be researched from secondary sources such as books or the Internet, or by interviewing a carer. The poster should include the following:

    - picture of a person who works in this role. This can be the real-life carer that the student has access to, or an imaginary case study. Students could source photos from a magazine

    - picture(s) of where they work

    - picture(s) of the sorts of people they work with

    - picture(s) of the sorts of equipment they have to use in their jobs

    - a list of the sorts of qualifications they might need or that they have to have before they can do their job

    - a list of the qualities that students think are necessary to do their job.

2. Once the posters are made, ask students to pin them up around the classroom. Now split the class in two. Ask the first group to be 'representatives' at the fair. Ask the second group to be 'customers' at the fair. The representatives should stand by their posters while the customers walk around the fair, examining them. The customers should ask the representatives suitable questions to find out more about the job roles. Students could be encouraged to ask 'What skills and qualities do you need to do this job?' and to consider whether it would suit them.

3. After 15 minutes, roles should be swapped, so that the first group of students can be 'customers' and the second group 'representatives'.

Extension activity

Following on from what they have learnt from the careers fair, ask students to write down between 100 and 150 words saying which job they think they would like to do and why they think they have the right skills and qualities for that job.

A day in the life of ...

Choose a job role from a health, social care or early years service and fill in the title above the table on the next page. Using secondary sources or by interviewing a real-life carer, prepare a timetable for a typical working day.

In the second column, write the tasks that the worker carries out. You might also want to include the following:

- how they get to work and how far they might have to travel
- any meetings (for example, a team briefing) that they attend
- the times when they have to write reports/records/emails and so on
- the times they take breaks
- whether they have to do the same tasks every day
- whether they take work home

As an **extension activity**, think about any **skills** or **care values** that the worker will need to have or apply as they do certain jobs. Write those alongside the tasks in the last column.

Here is the start of a timetable. This example is taken from the Folens *GCSE Health & Social Care* textbook. If you want, you could use this example to fill in the timetable.

A day in the life of a nursery nurse

Time	Task or event	Skill or care value applied
07:30	Leave home to drive to work.	
08:00	Arrive at work for a staff meeting.	Communication and listening skills applied.
08:15	Check nursery equipment that has been set out.	Keeping children safe and maintaining a safe environment care value applied.
08:30	Greet children as they arrive at nursery and ask parents about any special things that have happened or that they want me to do. Take a register.	Interpersonal skills applied. Promoting individual rights care value applied.

A day in the life of _____

Time	Task or event	Skill or care value applied

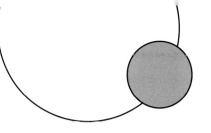

CHAPTER THREE: Promoting Health and Well-being

[Edexcel Unit 3; OCR Unit A913]

Introducing this chapter

'Promoting Health and Well-being' is an internally assessed unit. Students will benefit from the practical experience of assessing the health and well-being of themselves, another person such as a friend, colleague or a family member, or an individual/group of individuals from a pre-released case study.

Edexcel Unit 3

The topics covered are:

3.1 Understanding health and well-being

3.2 Factors affecting health and well-being

3.3 Indicators of physical health

3.4 Promoting and supporting health improvement

Edexcel assessment

This unit is internally assessed and externally moderated. Students will carry out one task, which will be based on pre-released material about an individual or group of individuals. The pre-released material will include information about the health and well-being of the individual(s), the factors currently affecting their health and well-being and data on their present health status.

Students will be expected to show knowledge of:

- definitions of health and well-being
- factors that affect health and well-being
- the effects of factors affecting health and well-being
- methods used to measure an individual's physical health
- ways of promoting and supporting health improvement.

In carrying out the task, students will demonstrate the ability to apply knowledge and understanding to promoting the health and well-being of an individual or group of individuals. Students will need to plan and carry out investigations based on the pre-released material and produce a health and well-being plan for an individual or group of individuals. In addition, they will be expected to analyse and evaluate information, draw conclusions and present reasoned judgements from the material presented in the pre-release.

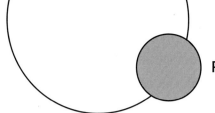

OCR Unit A913

The topics covered are:

3.3.1 Define the health and well-being of individuals

3.3.2 Interpret physical measures of health for individuals

3.3.3 Factors that have positively affected health and well-being

3.3.4 Risks to health and well-being

3.3.5 Health promotion and improvement methods

OCR assessment

This internally assessed unit is supported by a controlled assignment, which will be re-issued every two years. It benefits from access to work experience, visits to observe care workers in practice and visiting occupational speakers. For their evidence, students focus on services that are from one of the health, social care or early years sectors, for example:

- health, for example, health centre or hospital (private hospital or NHS)
- social care, for example, day centre for older people (local authority) or residential home (private)
- early years, for example, nursery, paediatric service or children's centre.

Notes on using this chapter

Health Promotion Units are no longer available to access for information; however, private or public leisure centres may offer excellent opportunities for students to gather evidence. The Internet also provides a vast range of addresses and references to enable students to build a literature library for their own or collective use (see worksheet 3.2).

It will also be of benefit if you can arrange a visit from a health professional, such as a practice nurse from a local surgery or a fitness trainer from a local fitness centre. The nurse or trainer should be approached several weeks before the preferred date for the presentation, at which time the precise agenda you want them to cover should be specified. For example, you could ask them to demonstrate the correct way to measure and interpret blood pressure, peak flow, body mass index, waist to hip ratios, and resting pulse and recovery rate after exercise. You will need to ask them to bring their own equipment for the demonstration in the class, for example, blood pressure and peak flow instruments, and make it clear that you would like your students to be able to use the equipment for testing themselves or others, which may entail the professional bringing additional equipment for this purpose.

For those of you who might find it difficult to arrange such a visit, we have provided some film clips on the accompanying CD-ROM.

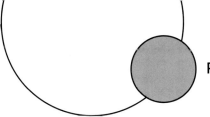

Table of contents for this chapter

Page	Resource no.	Resource title	Edexcel unit covered	OCR unit covered	Support resource
59		Introduction	Unit 3	Unit A913	
63	3.1	'Defining health and well-being' teacher-led activity	3.1	3.3.1	1. 'Definitions of health and well-being' ppt 3.1 (CD-ROM) 2. 'Definitions of health and well-being' interactive 3.1 (CD-ROM)
64	3.2	'Developing a literature library' teacher-led activity	Unit 3, particularly 3.4	Unit A913, particularly 3.3.5	1. 'List of leaflet suppliers' pdf 3.2 (CD-ROM) 2. 'List of leaflet suppliers' Word document 3.2 (CD-ROM)
65	3.3	'Designing a health questionnaire' teacher-led activity	Unit 3	Unit A913	'Designing a health questionnaire' ppt 3.3 (CD-ROM)
66	3.4(O)	'Factors that contribute to positive health' worksheet		3.3.3	Suggested answers on ppt 3.4(O) (CD-ROM)
67	3.5(E)	'Factors affecting health and well-being' worksheet	3.2		
68	3.6	'Risks to health' teacher-led activity	3.2	3.3.4	'Statements on health and well-being' information sheet (p69)
69	3.6	'Statements on health and well-being' information sheet	3.2	3.3.4	
70	3.7	'A balanced diet' worksheet	3.2	3.3.3	
71	3.8	'Physical measures of health' teacher-led activity	3.3	3.3.2	1. Film clip 3.8A to serve as an introduction (CD-ROM) 2. Film clips 3.8B–3.8F (CD-ROM) 3. 'Physical measures of health' worksheet (p72)
72	3.8	'Physical measures of health' worksheet	3.3	3.3.2	

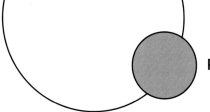

73	3.9(E)	'Measures of health bingo!' teacher-led activity	3.3	3.3.2	'Measures of health bingo!' worksheet (p75)
75	3.9(E)	'Measures of health bingo!' worksheet	3.3	3.3.2	
76	3.10	'Brian' case study	3.4	3.3.4, 3.3.5	
77	3.10	'What are the risks to Brian's health and well-being?' worksheet	3.4	3.3.4, 3.3.5	'Brian' case study (p76)
			Unit 3	Unit A913	'Revision quiz' interactive (CD-ROM)

Defining health and well-being

This activity asks students to consider how health is defined, and introduces positive, negative and holistic definitions of well-being.

Resources

- Flip chart or whiteboard.
- Stick-it notes.
- Pens.
- PowerPoint® 3.1 (CD-ROM).

Instructions

1. Use a flip chart or whiteboard and draw a large outline of a person. Offer each member of the group a stick-it note or other adhesive-backed paper and ask them to write their own brief definition of health and well-being. Allow collaboration and discussion in small groups for about ten minutes.

2. When ten minutes have passed, invite each participant to read out their definition and place it on the human outline that is displayed. The group discussion that follows could highlight the different definitions that may be negative, positive or holistic. There may also be some cultural or age-related differences.

3. Reinforce the students' work by showing **PowerPoint® 3.1** here. You could suggest that a student reads out the definition found on page 93 of the WHO (World Health Organization) manual, 'a state of complete physical, mental and social well-being, not merely the absence of disease and infirmity'. Candidates should discuss this definition.

Extension activity

Ask the group to research the following areas that relate to health and well-being:

a) What are the benefits and national recommendations of exercise?

b) Explore the importance of sleep and describe a normal sleep pattern.

c) How does alcohol affect a person's health and well-being? Are there recommended safe limits and, if so, what are they?

Developing a literature library

Many Health Promotion Units have been closed in recent years, but thanks to the Internet, access to leaflets and health information is possibly easier and more cost effective than before. The aim of this activity is to build up a library of resources for students to use as reference material throughout the unit. It should also help them to understand the importance of health promotion materials.

Resources

- Access to Internet facilities.
- List of leaflet suppliers (CD-ROM).
- A1 paper and materials to make a poster.

Instructions

1. Ask students, in groups of three, to collect and collate information leaflets on two of the following subjects in order to build up a class literature library (a list of suggested websites and contacts are provided on the CD-ROM).

Diet	Pregnant mothers
Exercise	The homeless
Alcohol	Diabetes
Smoking	Heart disease
Drugs	Older people
Young people	Stress
Unprotected sex	Sleep
Unemployment	Pollution
Poverty	Poor hygiene

2. After obtaining their leaflets and information, groups should produce a poster that illustrates health promotion for and information on their subject. The students can incorporate the leaflets they have gathered or use them merely as sources of information. The aim of the poster should be to support, inform and motivate people to improve their health and well-being, targeting a specific area.

Designing a health questionnaire

The aim of this activity is to offer students guidance on designing a health questionnaire.

Resources

- Pen and paper.
- PowerPoint® 3.3.
- IT facilities, if students wish to edit and type up the questionnaire.

Instructions

1. Divide the whole group into four sub-groups and ask each to design three questions for a proposed health questionnaire. Each sub-group could be given one of the following health aspects:

   Group 1: Physical (strength, stamina and suppleness). NB. Lifestyles, for example, smoking and alcohol, should be included in this aspect.
   Group 2: Intellectual (thinking, learning and decision making).
   Group 3: Emotional (personal feelings, for example, happiness, anger, stress and fear).
   Group 4: Social (interpersonal relationships, contact with family and friends).

2. Inform students that to obtain the information required, questions should be appropriate, that is, questions that students would be prepared to ask others or be willing to answer themselves. They should also be open questions wherever possible. Further guidance on questionnaire design and implementation can be found on **PowerPoint® 3.3** on the CD-ROM.

3. Allow 15 minutes for the sub-groups to design their questions. Each sub-group should then share their questions with the rest of the group, allowing the class to offer feedback. A first draft of the questionnaire can be drawn out of the discussion.

4. The questionnaire can be tested by splitting the whole group into pairs to act as interviewer and interviewee. The whole-group discussion that follows should aim to identify any difficult or uncomfortable questions that may need changing or re-designing.

Factors that contribute to positive health

Complete the spider diagram below either by discussing it as a whole group or working individually, using your textbook as a reference.

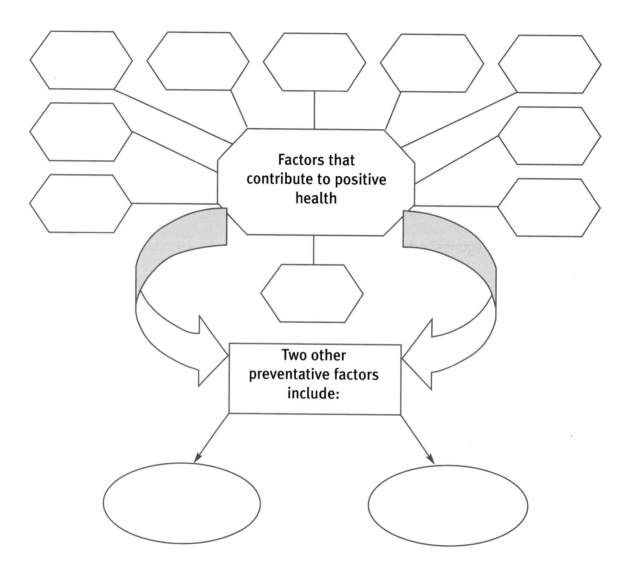

GCSE Health & Social Care

© Folens (copiable page)

Factors affecting health and well-being

The statements below are negative examples of factors affecting health and well-being.

Phuong is homeless	Paul is stressed about his exams	Jamil has lost contact with his family
Caroline has missed her appointment for a cervical smear test	Jessica suffers from cerebral palsy	Alice cannot afford to feed herself three meals a day

1. Can you identify what type of factor – physical, social, economic, and so on – each is an example of? Add each statement into the second column of the table below, next to the appropriate type of factor.

2. Can you think of factors that might make a positive contribution to health and well-being in each of the categories? Add those to the third column of the table. One example has been filled in for you.

Type of factor affecting health and well-being	Negative example (choose from examples above)	Positive example
Physical		A healthy, balanced diet
Social, cultural or emotional		
Economic		
Physical environment		
Psychological		
Health monitoring and illness-prevention service		

Risks to health

This is an interactive game to provoke thoughts and feelings concerning the risks to an individual's health and well-being.

Resources

- 'Statements on health and well-being' information sheet (p68).

Instructions

1. Prepare a set of cards with the statements from the information sheet, 'Statements on health and well-being'. They could be laminated and kept for future use.

2. Ask the whole group to form two equal rows facing each other, with a space down the middle. Place the card with 'STRONGLY AGREE' at one end of the rows and the card with 'STRONGLY DISAGREE' at the other end.

3. Read out one of the statements and offer it to the first person at the end of one of the rows. He/she can place the card on the floor anywhere along the line depending on how strongly they agree or disagree with the statement. Then, ask the rest of the group whether anyone differs in their feelings and, if they do, invite them to move the card in either direction. Finally, ask a third student who disagrees with the placement to move the card again. After this move it stays put.

4. Read all of the cards in turn and encourage all members to participate. Leave the cards in the positions selected by the group, which can then be referred to in subsequent discussion. This exercise is a useful warm up to identify factors affecting and risks to health. It can also highlight that we all differ in our opinions and that others may not always think the same way that we do.

Extension activity

Using a whiteboard or flip chart, ask the group to name the perceived risks to health, and list them in their perceived order of severity.

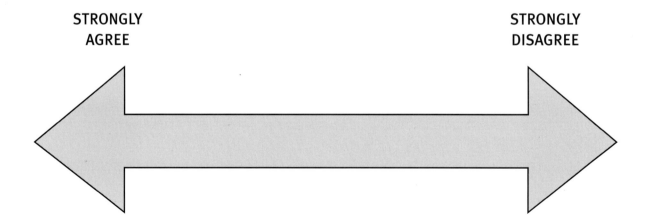

STRONGLY AGREE — STRONGLY DISAGREE

Statements on health and well-being

✂

1. Genetically inherited diseases are unimportant

2. Smoking is harder to give up than heroin

3. Alcohol can cause weight gain

4. Stress is good for us

5. A balanced diet is very important

6. Too much exercise can be bad for you

7. Friends and social activities can cause problems

8. Adequate housing and money to keep us out of debt are important

9. It's a bonus if you enjoy your work

10. We should monitor our health at all times

11. Risks are good for us

12. Personal hygiene is unimportant

13. Unprotected sex is not risky

14. We are not responsible for the environment

15. Sleep is the most restorative function of the body

STRONGLY AGREE

STRONGLY DISAGREE

A balanced diet

The image below shows the recommended portions of different types of food that we should eat to make up a balanced diet.

1. On a separate piece of paper, draw your own version of the eatwell plate and write down your favourite foods from each category.

2. The seven components in a healthy diet are:
   • protein
   • fat
   • carbohydrates
   • vitamins
   • minerals
   • water
   • fibre.

   Do you know which foods these components can be found in? Label your diagram to show which components the different food groups provide. Each component may go into more than one category.

Physical measures of health

The aim of this activity is to show students how the following measures of health are taken and why:

1. Blood pressure.
2. Peak flow.
3. Height and weight in relation to body mass index.
4. Waist to hip ratio.
5. Resting pulse and recovery rate after exercise.

Resources
- Film clips 3.8A – 3.8F (CD-ROM).
- 'Physical measures of health' worksheet (p71).
- Tape measures (one for each pair in your class).
- Stopwatch, or watch with a second hand (one for each pair in your class).

Instructions

1. You might want to invite a local health professional to lead this lesson. He/she should be approached in plenty of time and invited to introduce the importance of the above measurements and when they may be used. When arranging this visit, it would be helpful to ask the professional to provide the equipment needed to cover the subject. They should be asked to demonstrate the correct procedures for taking these measurements. They should also explain the importance of any abnormal readings, and any follow-up checks that may be necessary. Alternatively, show **film clips 3.8A–3.8F** supplied on the CD-ROM.

2. Hand out the 'Physical measures of health' worksheet so that students will know the information that they need to look out for. After watching the demonstration/film clips, ask students to answer the questions on the worksheet.

3. Now that they have been shown how, you could give your students the opportunity to take measurements for each other. Group students into pairs and provide tape measures for measuring waist to hip ratios.

4. The whole group, working in pairs, can now attempt to measure a pulse. A stopwatch (or clock with a second hand) should be made available for this exercise.

Extension activity

In collaboration with your PE department, you might be able to arrange for your group to check their fitness levels using the Harvard Step Test. This involves exercising, as directed, for four minutes and then monitoring the pulse rate after resting for one, two and three-and-a-half minutes.

Physical measures of health

After watching the demonstration, answer the following questions:

1. What two instruments do you need to take a manual blood pressure reading?

    i)..

    ii) ....

2. What is a 'normal' blood pressure reading? ....

3. Identify two conditions that may cause breathing difficulties.

    i)..

    ii)...

4. Circle the correct answer:

    When measuring peak flow we take

    i) the lowest reading

    ii) an average reading

    iii) the highest reading.

5. What does BMI stand for? ....

6. What is the formula for calculating BMI, including units of measurement?

    ....

7. What do you understand by the term 'waist to hip ratio'?

    ....

8. What can the waist to hip ratio measurement tell us?

    ....

9. What do we mean by 'recovery rate'?

    ....

10. Circle the correct answer:

    The fitter a person is …

    i) the quicker it takes their pulse reading to return to normal after exercise

    ii) the longer it takes their pulse reading to return to normal after exercise.

GCSE Health & Social Care © Folens (copiable page)

Measures of health bingo!

This is a fun activity that will check students' understanding of key terms related to measurements of health. This could be a good follow-on activity from worksheet 3.8, 'Physical measures of health', to reinforce learning.

Resources
- 'Measures of health bingo!' worksheet 3.9, one copy per student.
- Pens.

Instructions
1. Photocopy worksheet 3.9(E) and hand out a copy to each student in the class.

2. Ask students to fill in their bingo grids, picking words at random from the list of key terms.

3. Now start the game of bingo. Read out the definitions of key terms from the list below. You can mix up the order in which the definitions are read out if you like. When students recognize a key term, they should cross it from their grid.

4. When they have crossed out a whole line, students should be encouraged to hold up their hand and shout out 'Line!'

5. The winner of the game is the first person to cross out all the terms in their grid and then to shout out 'BINGO!' You should check the student's answer to make sure they have correctly identified the terms.

Key terms and definitions

Key term: Body mass index
Definition: The measurement of the relationship between an individual's height and weight

Key term: Sphygmomanometer
Definition: Equipment used to measure blood pressure

Key term: Body fat composition
Definition: The percentage of fat we carry in our bodies

Key term: Asthma
Definition: A respiratory disease that can cause difficulties with breathing

Key term: Peak flow meter
Definition: Equipment used to measure the maximum rate that someone can expel air from their lungs

Key term: Pulse
Definition: The force of the heart pumping blood around the arteries, felt as a pulsing sensation and measured in 'beats per minute'

Key term: Hypertension
Definition: High blood pressure

Key term: Waist to hip ratio
Definition: A measurement of health that considers the individual's body shape

Key term: Obese
Definition: A word to describe someone who weighs 20 per cent more than the average weight for someone of the same height

Key term: Diabetes
Definition: A condition that results in abnormally high blood sugar levels

Key term: Liver function test
Definition: Measurement from a blood sample to assist the diagnosis of liver disease

Key term: Cholesterol
Definition: A substance carried in your blood stream by high- and low-density lipoproteins

Key term: Recovery rate
Definition: The time it takes for the pulse rate to return to normal after exercise

Key term: Glucose
Definition: Blood sugar

Measures of health bingo!

Instructions:

- Choose nine of the key terms listed below and place them randomly in the blank grid.
- Your teacher will read out some definitions of key terms relating to measures of health. When you hear the definition of one of your key terms, cross it out.
- When you have crossed out a line from the grid, put up your hand and shout out 'LINE!'
- The winner is the first person to cross out all the terms from their grid, and then to shout out 'BINGO!'

Key terms:

Asthma   Body fat composition   Body mass index   Cholesterol

Diabetes   Glucose   Waist to hip ratio

Hypertension   Liver function test   Obese   Peak flow meter

Pulse   Recovery rate   Sphygmomanometer

Brian

Brian is 20 years of age. He lives at home with his mother, father and older sister. He left school at 16 and started working for a building firm. After a few months he complained of a painful back and began having time off work. This resulted in him losing his job and he hasn't tried to get other employment since. He spends most of his time sitting around and takes very little exercise. Brian relies on unemployment benefits, and his mother and father to provide his food and accommodation. His older sister is 24. She works long hours at a local hotel and contributes financially to her parents' housekeeping budget.

Brian's typical day starts about 10:30am when he gets out of bed and makes his own breakfast, usually something cooked, such as fried eggs, or a bacon sandwich with brown sauce. He drinks lots of tea in the morning and then cola throughout the rest of the day. In the afternoon, he will consume two or three bags of crisps and a large piece of cake while he watches television. His mother and father both work during the day but his mother cooks an evening meal for the whole family most days.

In the evening, Brian usually watches television for a while and then wanders down to the local pub for a game of darts and a few beers. When he arrives home, most of the family are in bed, or on their way. This is when Brian plays on the computer his mother bought for him to try and encourage him to have an interest. He is often on the Internet, frequenting 'chat rooms' and playing games until 2:00am or 3:00am. At home, he often smokes 10 to 15 cigarettes a day. His father used to smoke but had to give up after he had a heart attack when he was 50 years old. Brian is not very tall, measuring 1.72m (5' 8") and his weight has crept up in the last few years; he now weighs 91.7kg (14st 7lb).

Brian's sister is very unhappy because he does not contribute to the family budget and does not attempt to find work. There are often rows within the family that make each member unhappy.

GCSE Health & Social Care © Folens (copiable page)

What are the risks to Brian's health and well-being?

Read through the case study, 'Brian'. Individually, or in small groups, complete the following tasks.

1. Consider why a physical health assessment and target setting are important for Brian's immediate and long-term health and well-being. List all the risk factors in Brian's life.

2. Identify the risks to Brian's health in the long term if he continues with his current lifestyle. What are some of the illnesses he is at risk of developing? Write down as many as you can think of.

3. List the health checks that should be recommended to Brian.

4. Using the following chart, can you assess Brian's BMI?

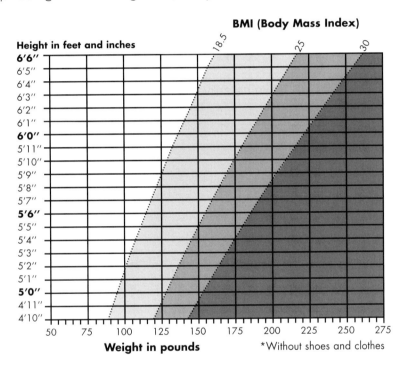

Direction: To use the BMI Chart, find the height on the vertical axis. Move across the row to the weight. Where the height and weight intersect, this is the BMI range.

Healthy weight: 18.5–25 BMI range indicates a healthy weight

Overweight: 25–30 BMI range indicates overweight

Obese: 30 BMI range and above indicates that a person is obese

NB. The BMI may not be sufficiently accurate for people with greater muscle mass, such as elite athletes.

5. Consider some health targets for Brian. Is it realistic that he will achieve them?

6. Discuss ways to encourage Brian to change his current lifestyle. Suggest people who you think may help to motivate Brian and some health promotion material that you would like to see available.

GCSE Health & Social Care © Folens (copiable page)

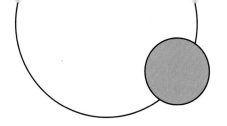

CHAPTER FOUR: Safeguarding and Protecting Individuals
[OCR Unit A914]

Introducing this chapter
'Safeguarding and Protecting Individuals' is an externally assessed unit that forms part of the Double Award specification only. The focus of the unit is to develop awareness of safeguarding and protecting individuals. Candidates need to consider who might be at risk, why some people are ill-treated and that anyone, from a professional carer to a relative, could be an abuser.

OCR Unit A914
The topics covered are:
- Safeguarding individuals
- Infection control
- First-aid practice
- How to recognize potential risks to safety and how to reduce risks in settings

OCR assessment
Assessment for this unit is through a 1-hour written examination or computer-based test with a total of 60 marks available.
- The paper will comprise of a series of questions requiring short to medium-length answers.
- All questions are compulsory. They will test knowledge and understanding, and the ability to apply that knowledge and understanding to a range of contexts through identification, description and explanation.
- The quality of written communication WILL be assessed throughout the written paper. Examiners will be looking for evidence of accurate spelling, punctuation, grammar and clarity of expression. Writing should be legible and meaning should be clear.
- Papers should be accessible to all students with questions and mark schemes being tiered to allow the weaker candidates to access marks even on the harder questions.

Notes on using this chapter
A practice paper is included at the end of this chapter so that students can test their knowledge and understanding of what they have learnt in it. Please note, this paper has not been through the usual OCR quality assurance procedures and, therefore, cannot be guaranteed as being an accurate reflection of the actual exam paper. A mark scheme can be found on the accompanying CD-ROM.

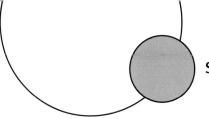

Table of contents for this chapter

Safeguarding individuals

The aim of this activity is to encourage learners to think about what constitutes abuse and what doesn't.

Resources

- The 'Safeguarding individuals' case study. It might be useful to photocopy and laminate this for future use.
- Answers can be found on PowerPoint® 4.1.

Instructions

1. Please note that this is a sensitive subject and you may have students in your class who could be affected by the discussions you will have. Introduce the topic carefully to the class and stress that if anyone does not wish to take part, they do not have to.

2. Divide the students into groups of three or four.

3. Give each group one of the scenarios on the 'Safeguarding individuals' case study.

4. Ask them to discuss the questions at the end of each case study in their groups.

5. Who might be an appropriate professional to involve in each case?

Plenary

Bring the group together and go through each scenario, discussing the students' thoughts.

Safeguarding individuals

Enid and George

The Willows is a residential care home caring for older adults who are suffering from dementia. Some residents tend to wander, several are very aggressive and a couple can even be violent. Over 75 per cent of the residents are incontinent. The staff try to take the residents to the toilet at regular intervals throughout the day.

One day, Enid's daughter came to visit her. As she was walking into the day room she heard the staff talking very loudly to Enid and George using phrases such as 'Come on Enid, time for a tinkle or we will have another puddle' and 'Oh George, you have pooed your pants again'. Enid's daughter complained to the local Care Home Inspection Unit.

In your group, discuss the following:

1. Do you think that the behaviour of the staff amounted to abuse?
2. If you do, why was it abusive?
3. What type of abuse do you think it was – physical, emotional, psychological, verbal, sexual, financial or neglect?
4. If you do not think it was abusive, why not?
5. How could Enid and George have been treated differently?

Christy

Christy is four years old. She was born several weeks early and has various medical problems. She has a squint in her left eye, one leg is slightly shorter than the other because her hip is unstable and she has a defect in the muscle wall of her heart known as a 'hole in the heart'.

Christy and her family have recently moved to a new village in North Yorkshire. Her new health visitor noted that Christy had not attended the hospital for any of her appointments to check her medical condition. She discussed the missed appointments with Christy's mother, who said that she did not feel they were necessary. The health visitor decided to report the case to the local Children and Young People's service (social services).

In your group, discuss the following:

1. Do you think that by not taking Christy to her medical appointments, Christy's mother was abusing her daughter?
2. If you do, why was it abusive?
3. What type of abuse do you think it was – physical, emotional, psychological, verbal, sexual, financial or neglect?
4. If you do not think it was abusive, why not?
5. What action should be taken, if any?

Alan

Alan is 23 years of age and attends a day centre for people with learning disabilities. The staff at the day centre are encouraging Alan to become as independent as possible so that, hopefully, in the future, he will be able to live in his own flat.

Last week, Sandra, Alan's key worker, took him shopping to buy some new clothes. Alan chose his clothes and then asked Sandra for some money to pay for them. Sandra refused to give Alan his own money and said that she would pay for the clothes because Alan could not be trusted with the cash. Alan became extremely angry. Sandra grabbed him by the arm and pushed him out of the shop, shouting at him that he had embarrassed her and could not have any new clothes.

In your group, discuss the following:

1. Do you think that Sandra's actions amounted to abuse?
2. If you do, why was it abusive?
3. What type of abuse do you think it was – physical, emotional, psychological, verbal, sexual, financial or neglect?
4. If you do not think it was abusive, why not?
5. How could Alan have been treated differently?

Ryan

Ryan is six years of age. His parents, Robert and Mandy, have two other children, Daniel, who is three years of age and Megan, who is 14 months. The whole family are dedicated Jehovah's Witnesses, which is a Christian religious movement.

A few weeks ago, Ryan was diagnosed with leukaemia. The doctors have told Robert and Mandy that if Ryan is to stand any chance of recovery, he must have a blood transfusion. One of the key beliefs of Jehovah's Witnesses is that it is wrong to accept a blood transfusion under any circumstances and, therefore, Ryan's parents have refused to let Ryan have one. Ryan's condition is gradually becoming worse and the doctors have said that he will not survive if he does not receive some blood soon.

In your group, discuss the following:

1. Do you think that Ryan's parents are abusing Ryan by not letting him have a blood transfusion?
2. If you do, why do you think their actions are abusive?
3. What type of abuse do you think it is – physical, emotional, psychological, verbal, sexual, financial or neglect?
4. If you do not think it is abusive, why not?
5. Should the doctors do anything about Ryan's condition?

Mrs Patel

Mrs Patel is 76 years of age. She lives alone in sheltered housing. Last week, when her daughter, Ghariba, came to visit, Mrs Patel was very distressed. She told Ghariba that she was being harassed and intimidated by a male neighbour. He has also called her racist names.

Ghariba spoke to the warden and told her that she wanted something done about the male neighbour. The warden said she would investigate and a week later she referred Mrs Patel to the social services' safeguarding team.

In your group, discuss the following:

1. Do you think that the neighbour's behaviour amounted to abuse?
2. If you do, why was it abusive?
3. What type of abuse do you think it was – physical, emotional, psychological, verbal, sexual, financial or neglect?
4. If you do not think it was abusive, why not?
5. What do you think should be done about the neighbour?

Michael

Michael is 11. His parents are separated and he lives with his mother, Wendy. At weekends, Michael goes to stay at his father's house in the next town. When Michael is there, his father regularly rents out '18' rated videos and games for his games console from the local video store. He encourages Michael to join him in watching the videos and playing the games, even though some of the games are very violent and the films have a large sexual content.

Over the past few months, Wendy has noticed that Michael is regularly having nightmares. She talked to him and Michael told her about the games and the videos.

In your group, discuss the following:

1. Do you think that Michael's father's actions amount to abuse?
2. If you do, why was it abusive?
3. What type of abuse do you think it was – physical, emotional, psychological, verbal, sexual, financial or neglect?
4. If you do not think it was abusive, why not?
5. What action should be taken, if any?

Amelia

Amelia is ten years of age. She lives at home with her parents, David and Julie, and her sisters, Olivia, aged five, and Charlotte, aged three. David works full time as a bus driver and Julie works part time in a call centre. Usually, David gets home before Julie has to go to work. Recently, however, the family have been short of money and so David has been doing some overtime. This has meant that Julie has had to go to work before David has returned home and she has left Amelia to look after Olivia and Charlotte until David returns.

In your group, discuss the following:

1. Do you think Amelia, Olivia and Charlotte are living in an abusive situation?
2. If you think they are, give some reasons why you think this.
3. What type of abuse do you think it is – physical, emotional, psychological, verbal, sexual, financial or neglect?
4. If you do not think it is abusive, why not?
5. What action should be taken, if any?

Becky

Becky is 16 years of age. She has been going out with Simon for 18 months. None of Becky's friends like Simon but Becky says that she does not want to leave him. Simon won't let Becky see any of her friends outside of school. He tells her that she is nothing without him and if she says she wants to go out with her girlfriends, Simon calls her a 'slut' and a 'tramp'. Simon makes all Becky's decisions for her. When Simon and Becky go out, if she even glances at another boy, Simon gets really mad and shouts at her.

In your group, discuss the following:

1. Do you think Becky is in an abusive situation?
2. If you think she is, give some reasons why you think so.
3. What type of abuse do you think it is – physical, emotional, psychological, verbal, sexual, financial or neglect?
4. If you do not think it is abusive, why not?
5. What action should be taken, if any?

Safeguarding individuals quiz

Answer the following questions on safeguarding individuals.

1. Who is responsible for ensuring the safety and well-being of children?

   a) Social workers

   b) The police

   c) Teachers

   d) Everybody

2. Individuals are only harmed by physical abuse.

   a) True

   b) False

3. Only men sexually abuse.

   a) True

   b) False

4. Children don't usually tell others that they are abused because:

   a) They don't think they will be believed.

   b) They are frightened.

   c) They may love their abuser.

   d) All of the above.

5. What are the government guidelines that cover work with child protection called?

   a) The Mental Health Act 2007

   b) The Children Act 2004

   c) The NHS and Community Care Act 1990

   d) Data Protection Act 1998

6. All age groups are safeguarded from abuse by legislation.

   a) True

   b) False

7. People can only be abused by individuals.

   a) True

   b) False

8. What should you do if you suspect a client in the residential home you are working in is being abused?

   a) Nothing, someone else will report it.

   b) Tell your friend.

   c) Tell your supervisor or teacher.

   d) Talk to the client.

9. A vulnerable adult could be abused by:

   a) A carer.

   b) Another service user.

   c) A family member.

   d) All of the above.

10. Bruises are not always an indication of physical abuse.

   a) True

   b) False

Infection control

Below are a set of general hygiene rules, which are important to observe at all times, especially when you are working in a care setting. For each one, give a brief explanation of why it is important. The first one has been done for you.

1. Wash your hands after using the toilet.

   Because bacteria and viruses, which cause gastro-intestinal infections, can be passed from one person to another if hands are not washed properly.

2. Store food in the fridge at the correct temperature.

   ....

   ....

   ....

3. Make sure frozen meat is thoroughly defrosted before cooking.

   ....

   ....

   ....

4. Wash hands after touching animals or animal waste.

   ....

   ....

   ....

5. Keep fingernails short and clean.

   ....

   ....

   ....

6. Keep cuts and grazes covered with a blue waterproof dressing when preparing food.

   ....

   ....

   ....

Hand washing

Your teacher will show you a film clip showing the correct technique for hand washing.

Can you fill in the gaps in the flowchart below?

Wet hands and apply soap. Then:

1. Massage palm to palm.

▼

2. ....
....

▼

3. ....
....

▼

4. Massage the back of your right fingers in the palm of your left hand and vice versa.

▼

5. ....
....

▼

6. ....
....

▼

Finally, rinse hands with water.

When done correctly, hand washing can help to prevent the spread of infection. List three instances when we should wash our hands, for example, before preparing food.

1. ....

2. ....

3. ....

First-aid procedures

Your teacher will show you **film clip 4.5A** showing the correct procedure for putting someone in the recovery position.

When might you need to put someone in the recovery position?

....

Below are illustrations of the steps for putting someone in the recovery position. After watching the video, write a sentence or two underneath the pictures to explain each step.

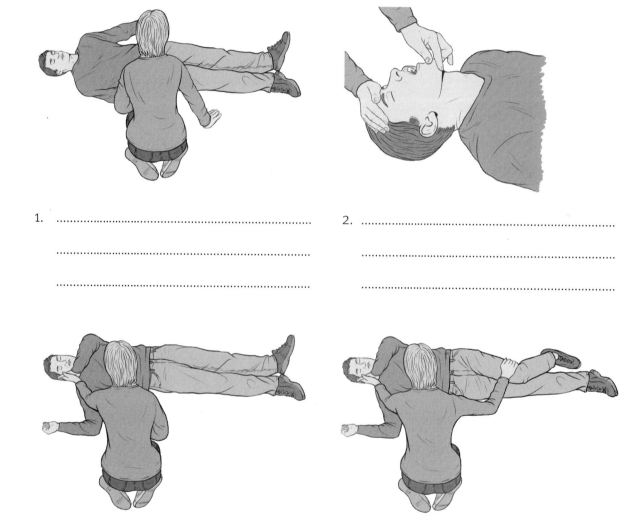

1. ....

....

....

2. ....

....

....

3. ....

....

....

4. ....

....

....

5. ....

....

....

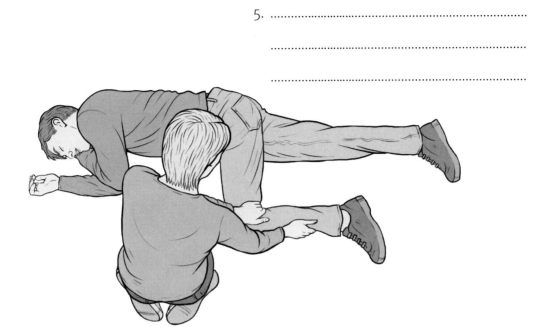

Here is an illustration of another first-aid procedure.

6. What is the name of this procedure? ....

7. When would you need to use it? ....

....

Your teacher can show you **film clip 4.5B** to demonstrate this technique.

First-aid wordsearch

Find the first-aid related words or phrases in the wordsearch below.

Tip: there are 23 to find.

A	E	E	M	E	R	G	E	N	C	Y	C	C	Z	A	A	C	U
A	I	R	B	B	U	G	E	C	Y	E	Y	I	D	B	U	R	N
Z	P	R	E	S	S	U	R	E	T	T	T	O	U	T	R	E	C
V	I	E	W	B	M	N	O	T	E	A	C	R	S	O	T	U	O
E	O	I	U	A	Y	T	R	F	E	V	W	Q	X	L	W	V	N
R	P	L	K	J	Y	H	A	G	F	E	D	Y	K	C	O	H	S
U	S	A	Z	X	C	S	V	B	N	L	G	R	M	N	B	V	C
T	N	N	O	S	I	O	P	E	G	E	W	E	A	C	X	C	I
C	W	V	G	I	N	M	A	I	N	E	T	T	N	N	O	P	O
A	M	A	M	I	O	G	N	I	H	G	F	R	D	S	A	D	U
R	B	S	D	N	S	C	E	D	X	C	Y	A	N	O	S	I	S
F	D	R	L	G	E	L	E	V	A	Y	R	T	H	R	O	A	D
F	E	P	A	I	B	U	P	R	A	D	H	I	S	T	O	T	I
R	S	F	C	R	L	U	G	Y	N	P	V	P	G	N	I	S	A
B	L	I	S	T	E	R	R	Y	T	L	A	U	S	A	C	R	G
N	U	R	S	D	E	U	N	V	E	E	N	M	W	A	A	I	N
R	P	S	O	P	D	I	A	R	R	H	O	E	A	P	S	F	P

Once you have identified all the words, write a brief definition or description of each one, stating why it is important in first aid.

The first one has been done for you:

First aid: *the immediate assistance given to someone injured or suddenly taken ill before the arrival of an ambulance, doctor or other suitably qualified person.*

Legislation

The aim of this activity is to introduce the key concepts of the various pieces of legislation relevant to protecting service users and care workers.

Resources

- PowerPoint® 4.7.
- Access to IT facilities.

Instructions

1. Split the group into pairs or groups of three.

2. Allocate each pair one piece of legislation as detailed in the specification or on **PowerPoint® 4.7.**

3. Allow between one and two hours for each pair to investigate their legislation and identify three key aspects of the legislation that protect service users or care workers.

4. During this time, each pair should also design a short PowerPoint® presentation, describing the three key features and giving an example of how they might be applied in the care setting. For example, the Health and Safety at Work Act 1974 – one key feature is that the employer must consider what could cause harm to people and how to take precautions. This would be applied by undertaking a risk assessment.

5. Each pair should then present their work to the whole group, providing handouts for the rest of the class.

Extension activity

As an extension activity you could ask the class to apply some basic evaluation skills. Consider the various pieces of legislation as a whole class and discuss whether the group thinks the legislation is effective in protecting service users/care workers. The group will need to look at the strengths, for example, the benefits to the service users/care workers, and the weaknesses, for example, where the legislation fails to protect the service users/care workers. Finally, the group will need to draw some relevant conclusions from their discussions.

Safety information signs

All care settings must display a range of signs that inform service users, care workers and visitors of safety information in the event of an emergency.

Can you match the TYPES of signs below with the kind of information that they give?

The first one has been done for you.

Type of sign	Meaning
Blue and white, for example:	Signs that warn of danger.
Green signs, for example:	Safe condition signs – it is safe to do something in an emergency.
A red ring shape with a line through it, for example:	Mandatory – signs that mean you MUST do something.
Yellow/orange signs, for example:	Signs that mean you MUST NOT do something.

Now, can you identify the signs below? Match the correct instruction to each safety sign.

Safety sign		Instruction
⚠️ corrosive symbol		No smoking
☎️ telephone symbol		Toxic material
🥾 safety boots symbol		Emergency telephone for first aid or escape
☠️ skull symbol		First aid post
🚭 no smoking symbol		No access for pedestrians
💥 explosive symbol		Safety boots must be worn
🚷 no pedestrians symbol		Explosive material
➕ first aid cross symbol		Corrosive material

GCSE Health & Social Care   © Folens (copiable page)

Safety sign	Instruction
	Overhead load
	Radioactive material
	Stretcher
	Respiratory equipment must be worn
	Eye protection must be worn
	Smoking and naked flames forbidden
	Not drinkable
	Flammable material or high temperature

What to do in the event of a fire

You are working in a residential care home as part of your GCSE Health and Social Care practical experience. You have been left in the day room with 20 residents while the care assistant goes to the kitchen to make a cup of coffee. One of the residents calls you over and says she can see smoke coming from behind the television. You go over to investigate and see dense smoke coming from the television.

1. Complete the second column below, to show whether the actions should be taken or not, by writing 'True' or 'False' next to each one.

2. When you have decided which statements are 'True', put the actions in order by numbering them 1–6 in the third column, to show the correct procedure.

Action	True or false	Order of procedure
Immediately panic and run out of the day room screaming.		
If it is safe to do so, combat the fire with the correct fire extinguisher.		
Inform the telephonist or dial 999.		
Do not return to the building for any reason.		
Raise the alarm.		
Go back into the building to collect your bag and coat before leaving.		
Go to the fire assembly point.		
Start helping the residents out of the danger area.		
Use the lift to get downstairs.		
Use a 'red' coded fire extinguisher.		

Undertaking a risk assessment

1. Using the template on the next page, complete the risk assessment for either:

    a) the floor plan of a day nursery (below)

    b) a classroom or communal area in your school or college.

An example of a hazard in the day nursery has been filled in for you. You should be able to think of lots more risks for either the day nursery or the location that you have chosen to consider.

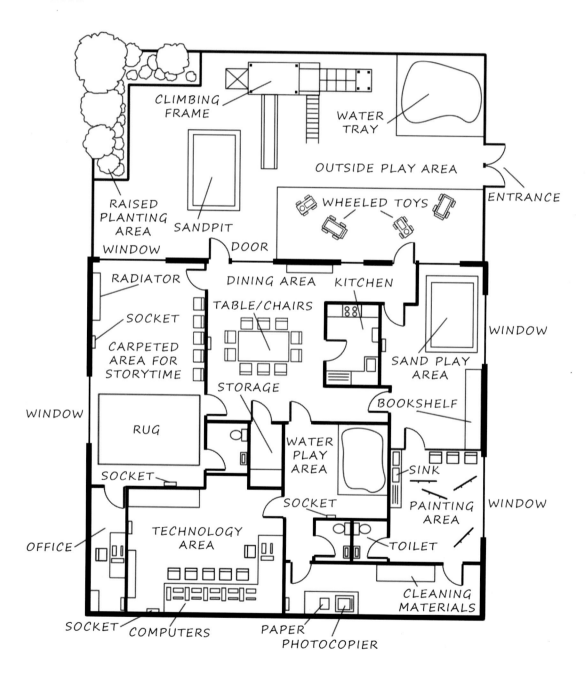

Risk-assessment form

Hazard/activity	Person at risk	How they may be harmed	Control measures to avoid an accident	Risk rating (high, medium or low)	Comments
Outside play area	Children and staff	Slips, trips, falls, cuts	In icy conditions, surface needs to be gritted or be placed out of bounds.	Low – medium	Grit in store cupboard. Check stocks each winter.

Folens' Practice Test for OCR

Time allowed: 1 hour

Instructions

- Use **BLACK** ink or ballpoint pen.

- Answer **ALL** the questions.

- Answer the questions in the space provided – there may be more space than you need.

Information

- The total mark for this paper is 60.

- The marks for **each** question are shown in brackets at the end of each question or part question – use this as a guide as to how much time to spend on each question.

Advice

- Read each question carefully and make sure you know what you have to do before starting your answer.

- Keep an eye on the time.

- Try to answer every question.

- Check your answers if you have time at the end.

1. Name **two** categories of abuse that an older person could be subjected to.

   1. ....

   2. .... (2)

2. Name a service user group that is safeguarded and protected by legislation.

   .... (1)

3. Identify which colour chopping board you would use for preparing the following foods:

   Raw meat ....

   Fish .... (2)

4. Name one substance, which might be found in a residential care home, that would be subject to the Control of Substances Hazardous to Health (COSHH) Regulations 2005.

   .... (1)

5. Identify each sign below.

| A | B | C |

   A ....

   B ....

   C .... (3)

6. Identify **two** security measures that a day nursery could introduce to keep children safe.

1. ....

2. ....　(2)

7. Describe **one** priority for a first aider when attending an accident.

....

....　(2)

8. Explain how 'indirect pressure' may be used to stop bleeding from a wound on the lower arm.

....

....

....

....　(4)

9. Identify **three** actions that a first aider should take when arriving at the scene of an accident and explain why each is important.

1. ....

....

....

2. ....

....

....

3. ....

....

....　(6)

10. Describe **two** methods of preventing the spread of infection in a hospital ward.

1. ....

   ....

   ....

   ....

2. ....

   ....

   ....

   ....   (4)

11. Explain why you think an infant school might have a 'Signing-in book' for visitors at reception.

....

....

....

....

....

....

....

....   (5)

GCSE **Health & Social Care** © Folens (copiable page)

12. Explain how the Children Act 2004 could help to safeguard children.

....

....

....

....

....

....

....

....

....

....

....

....

....

....

....   (8)

13. Identify **four** diseases that can be prevented through the national immunization programme.

1. ....

2. ....

3. ....

4. ....   (4)

GCSE Health & Social Care   © Folens (copiable page)

14. Evaluate the use of a vaccination programme in protecting babies against infectious diseases.

....

....

....

....

....

....

....

....

....

....

....

....

....

....

....   (8)

GCSE Health & Social Care   © Folens (copiable page)

Plan of a nursery classroom

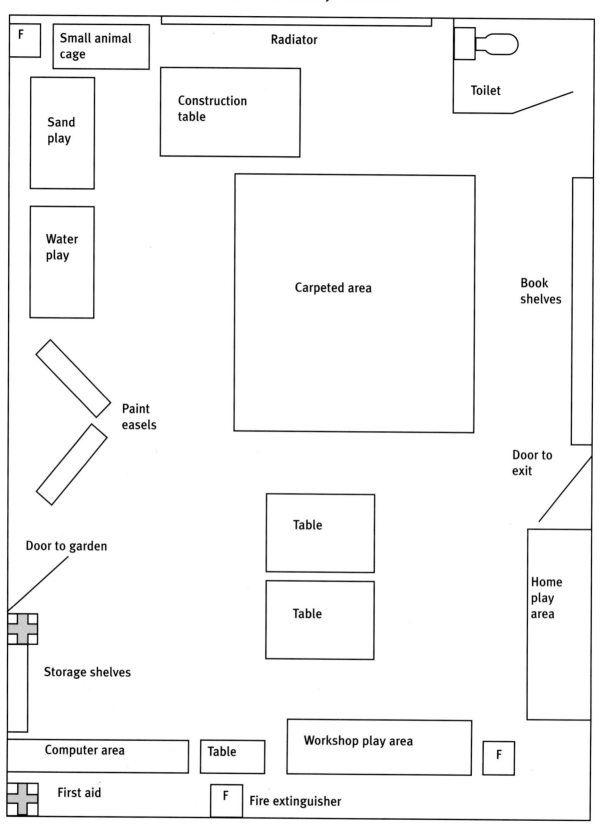

F

Small animal cage

Radiator

Toilet

Sand play

Construction table

Water play

Carpeted area

Book shelves

Paint easels

Door to exit

Door to garden

Table

Home play area

Table

Storage shelves

Workshop play area

F

Computer area

Table

First aid

F   Fire extinguisher

15. Carry out a risk assessment for the nursery classroom shown on the previous page.

You need to:

• look for hazards

• think about who may be at risk

• consider the risks – whether precautions are adequate.

....

....

....

....

....

....

....

....

....

....

....

....

....

....

....

....

.... (8)

TOTAL FOR PAPER = 60 MARKS

GCSE Health & Social Care © Folens (copiable page)

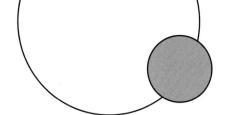

CHAPTER FIVE: Health, Social Care and Early Years in Practice

[Edexcel Unit 4]

Introducing this chapter

'Health, Social Care and Early Years in Practice' is an externally tested unit and requires learners to draw on knowledge and understanding of the core principles that underpin the work of practitioners in health, social care and early years settings (care and education), and in the care of individuals with specific needs. This is a synoptic unit that draws on knowledge learnt in Units 1, 2 and 3.

Edexcel Unit 4

The topics covered are:

4.1 The range of care needs of major client groups
4.2 Care values commonly used in practitioner work
4.3 The development of self-concept and personal relationships
4.4 Promoting and supporting health improvement

Edexcel assessment

Assessment for this unit is through a 75-minute written examination with a total of 70 marks available. The paper comprises of three questions based on case studies and short scenarios requiring short to medium-length answers.

- All questions are compulsory and will test knowledge and understanding and the ability to apply that knowledge and understanding to a range of contexts. Students will need to analyse and evaluate issues and problems, and draw reasoned conclusions from the material presented.
- The quality of written communication WILL be assessed throughout the written paper. Students will be guided via the rubrics of the paper as to which questions will be used to assess written communication. Examiners will be looking for evidence of accurate spelling, punctuation, grammar and clarity of expression.
- Papers should be accessible to all students with questions and mark schemes being tiered to allow the weaker candidates to access marks even on the harder questions.

Notes on using this chapter

Several of these topics have already been covered in Units 1, 2 and 3. Revision of the following topics will be of use:

1.1; 1.2; 1.3; 1.4
2.1; 2.4; 2.5
3.2; 3.4

A practice paper is included at the end of this unit so that students can test their knowledge and understanding of what they have learnt in it. Please note, this paper has not been through the usual Edexcel quality assurance procedures and, therefore, cannot be guaranteed as being an accurate reflection of the actual exam paper. A mark scheme can be found on the accompanying CD-ROM.

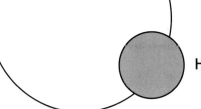

Table of contents for this chapter

Page	Resource no.	Resource title	Edexcel unit covered	OCR unit covered	Support resource
108		Introduction	Unit 4		
110	5.1	'Care needs' worksheet	4.1		Suggested answers on ppt 5.1 (CD-ROM)
111	5.2	'Tyler' case study	4.1, 4.2		
112	5.2	'Tyler's care needs' worksheet	4.1, 4.2		'Tyler' case study (p111)
113	5.3	'Lifestyle choices' worksheet	4.1		
114	5.4	'Care values' worksheet	4.2		1. 'Tyler' case study (p111) 2. 'Care values' on ppt 5.4 (CD-ROM)
115	5.5	'Discrimination' worksheet	4.2		Suggested answers on ppt 5.5 (CD-ROM)
116	5.6	'Jared – discrimination and self-esteem' worksheet	4.2, 4.3		
117	5.7	'Self-concept' worksheet	4.3		Suggested answers on ppt 5.7 (CD-ROM)
118	5.8	'Providing support' case study	4.2, 4.4		
120	5.8	'Care values and health promotion' teacher-led activity	4.2, 4.4		1. 'Providing support' case study (pp118–119) 2. Ppt 5.8 (CD-ROM)
121	5.9	'Health promotion' teacher-led activity	4.4		Ppt 5.9 (CD-ROM)
122	5.10	'Does health promotion really work?' teacher-led activity	4.4		1. 'BMI and smoking statistics' information sheet 2. Suggested answers on ppt 5.10 (CD-ROM)
123	5.10	'BMI and smoking statistics' information sheet	4.4		
124		Folens' Practice Test for Edexcel	Unit 4		1. 'Mark scheme' pdf (CD-ROM) 2. 'Key terms revision' interactive (CD-ROM) 3. 'Revision quiz' interactive (CD-ROM)

Care needs

Care needs can be split into four areas:

Physical   **Intellectual**   **Emotional**   **Social**

Complete the table below, identifying which area of physical, intellectual, emotional or social needs each example fits into. The first one has been completed for you.

Need	Area of P.I.E.S.
Food	Physical
Sense of belonging	
To feel loved	
Warmth	
Hobby or interest	
Security	
Clear boundaries for behaviour	
Shelter	
Having routines	
Having friends	
Mental stimulation	
Respect	

Tyler

Tyler is almost three years of age. His mum, Chelsea, has had to return to work and takes Tyler to a local day nursery three days each week. When Chelsea first approached the nursery, Mrs White, the nursery manager, filled in several forms that asked for details such as Tyler's name and address, any medical conditions, Chelsea's emergency contact details, and any special interests, fears or favourite toys. Mrs White informed Chelsea that this information would only be shared with Anna and Claire, the two nursery nurses.

Tyler has been attending the nursery for two weeks and still cries when his mum leaves him in the morning. At this time in the morning, Anna and Claire are always very busy and, sometimes, Tyler is just left to cry while the nursery nurses are getting ready for the day's activities.

The meals provided by the nursery are all freshly cooked and very healthy. In the morning, the children are also given a snack of fresh fruit. At lunchtime, Claire encourages Tyler to use his fork and spoon to eat his meals and gives him a drink in his own cup, which his mum brings in from home. She always asks Tyler what he would like to drink.

Tyler does not have any brothers or sisters, so Claire encourages him to play with the other children in the nursery. Tyler does not like sharing the toys with the other children and on three occasions since he started at the nursery he has hit another child when he wanted a particular toy. The nursery has a 'Behaviour policy', which states that all children should be treated exactly the same when they are naughty. When he misbehaves in this way, Tyler is asked to sit on a chair and is not allowed to play with any toys. Claire always gets down to Tyler's level and tries to explain to him that it is naughty to hit other children. After a few minutes, Claire welcomes Tyler back into the group, asks him to apologize and then allows him to play again.

Anna and Claire have devised a timetable of activities for the children to do every day. These activities can include reading stories, playing in the outdoor play area, singing and painting. Today they are painting Diwali cards.

One day, while at the nursery, Tyler was climbing on the climbing frame in the outdoor play area when he fell off and hurt his arm. Anna called his mum and asked her to take Tyler to hospital. Tyler had broken his arm and when he returned to nursery the next day, his right arm was in a plaster cast. Mrs White checked the climbing frame to ensure that it was safe for the other children to play on. She was pleased that the outdoor play area had a soft safety surface around all the equipment.

Tyler's care needs

Using the case study 'Tyler', complete the activities below:

1. Identify Tyler's current life stage.

   ....

2. Complete the table below, identifying the physical, intellectual, emotional and social needs that Tyler has in his current life stage and then stating how the nursery are meeting these needs.

Physical needs	How are these needs being met?
Intellectual needs	
Emotional needs	
Social needs	

3. Which area of Tyler's needs is not being met sufficiently?

   ....

4. Write a paragraph about how you think the nursery could better meet those needs.

Lifestyle choices

As a class, discuss the following questions:

1. What lifestyle choices is each of the individuals making?

2. Are they positive or negative lifestyle choices?

3. Does each person pictured above have the same opportunity to make healthy lifestyle choices? Consider the first picture carefully – how many people are there in this picture?

GCSE Health & Social Care © Folens (copiable page)

Care values

The Care Value Base is a group of five interconnected values that help carers provide the very best care by recognizing that each person is an individual and has both their own rights and their own care needs.

Identify the five key values that make up the Care Value Base by completing the following:

1. PROMOTING ANTI-D _ _ _ _ _ _ _ _ _ _ _ _ _ PRACTICE

2. PROMOTING AND SUPPORTING INDIVIDUAL R _ _ _ _ _ TO DIGNITY, I _ _ _ _ _ _ _ _ _ _ _ _ ,

    HEALTH AND S_ _ _ _ _

3. PROMOTING EFFECTIVE C _ _ _ _ _ _ _ _ _ _ _ _ AND R _ _ _ _ _ _ _ _ _ _ _

4. MAINTAINING C _ _ _ _ _ _ _ _ _ _ _ _ _ _ OF INFORMATION

5. ACKNOWLEDGING INDIVIDUAL PERSONAL B _ _ _ _ _ _ AND I _ _ _ _ _ _ _

Now look back at the 'Tyler' case study. For each of the principles of the Care Value Base you have identified above, find an example of where the day nursery puts this into practice and complete the table below.

	Care value	Example
1	PROMOTING ANTI- D _ _ _ _ _ _ _ _ _ _ _ _ _ PRACTICE	
2	PROMOTING AND SUPPORTING INDIVIDUAL R _ _ _ _ _ TO DIGNITY, I _ _ _ _ _ _ _ _ _ _ , HEALTH AND S _ _ _ _ _	
3	PROMOTING EFFECTIVE C _ _ _ _ _ _ _ _ _ _ _ AND R _ _ _ _ _ _ _ _ _ _	
4	MAINTAINING C _ _ _ _ _ _ _ _ _ _ _ _ _ _ OF INFORMATION	
5	ACKNOWLEDGING INDIVIDUAL PERSONAL B _ _ _ _ _ _ AND I _ _ _ _ _ _ _	

Discrimination

Many people who have a disability are discriminated against because they are 'different'.
On your own, or in a group, complete the following worksheet.

1. What do you understand by the term 'discrimination'?

    ....

    ....

    ....

    ....

2. There are two different types of discrimination. Fill in the gaps below to identify each one
    and give an example to show that you understand the difference.

    (i) D _ _ _ _ _ discrimination

         Example:

         ....

         ....

         ....

         ....

    (ii) I _ _ _ _ _ _ _ discrimination

         Example:

         ....

         ....

         ....

         ....

Jared – discrimination and self-esteem

Jared is four years of age and has a condition known as Down's syndrome. Down's syndrome is caused by a fault in the chromosomes, the basic structures that carry our genes and determine both who we are and how our body functions. It affects Jared's ability to learn. His mum would like him to go to the local infant school when he is five. A neighbour, whose little girl, Katy, is also due to start school with Jared, has complained to the school, saying that if Jared is in the same class as Katy the teachers will have to spend too much time with him and Katy will not get the attention she needs.

1. Do you think Katy's mum is right in her view? Give a reason for your answer.

   ....

   ....

   ....

   ....

2. What effect do you think this attitude could have on Jared's self-esteem? Give a reason for your answer.

   ....

   ....

   ....

   ....

3. How could the teachers use the care values to ensure that Jared is not discriminated against?

   ....

   ....

   ....

   ....

Self-concept

1. Unscramble the following words to complete the list of some of the factors that can affect our self-concept.

gea	repacpeana	lucurte
nudeaciot	dernge	efil pierexescen
spihsnoitaler thiw stehor		lesuax tintinoaore
cilaso slacs		tomaleion montleveped

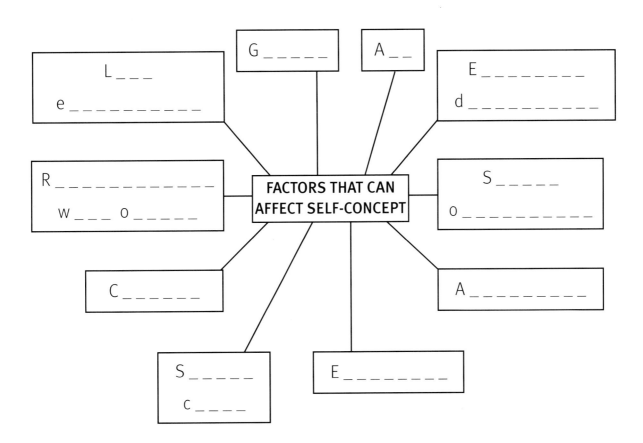

L _ _ _
e _ _ _ _ _ _ _ _ _ _

G _ _ _ _ _

A _ _

E _ _ _ _ _ _ _ _
d _ _ _ _ _ _ _ _ _ _

R _ _ _ _ _ _ _ _ _ _ _ _
W _ _ _ O _ _ _ _ _

FACTORS THAT CAN AFFECT SELF-CONCEPT

S _ _ _ _ _
O _ _ _ _ _ _ _ _ _

C _ _ _ _ _ _

A _ _ _ _ _ _ _ _ _

S _ _ _ _ _
c _ _ _ _ _

E _ _ _ _ _ _ _ _

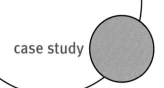
Providing support

Mrs Smith

Mrs Smith has been asked by her health visitor to make an appointment at the doctor's surgery for one-year-old Jason to have his 'Measles, Mumps and Rubella' (MMR) immunization. Mrs Smith has read an article about the MMR vaccine and has decided not to let Jason have it. The health visitor informs Mrs Smith of the benefits but she still decides not to go ahead. The health visitor accepts Mrs Smith's decision.

Gemma

Gemma is 18 years of age. She weighs 90kg and has a BMI of 34.1. Gemma is very depressed about her weight. She has made an appointment with her doctor to discuss the range of possibilities to help her lose weight. The doctor tells her that she has a variety of options that he could suggest: she could see a dietitian, she could attend Weight Watchers or she could go to the local gym for six months. He also mentions that he would like her to see a counsellor as he feels this would help with her depression. He asks her to make an appointment to see him next week to let him know which option she would like to take.

Mrs Harrison

Mrs Harrison is expecting her first baby in three months time. She has been invited to an antenatal class where the midwife will be discussing how to feed the baby after it is born. The midwife would like every mother to breastfeed their child as she knows this is best for the baby. She tells the group, including Mrs Harrison, all the benefits of breastfeeding but does not mention bottle feeding. She shows a DVD of a baby breastfeeding and gives out some leaflets. At the end of the session, Mrs Harrison tells the midwife that she will be bottle feeding her baby because this is what all her family have done in the past. The midwife says that if Mrs Harrison has any questions about bottle feeding she would be happy to answer them.

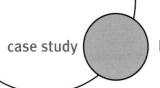
Health visiting team

The health visiting team at the local health clinic have decided to run a week-long campaign in the local shopping centre advising people on the dangers of smoking and on different types of help to stop smoking. This campaign is running at the same time as a series of government-funded adverts on the television and a government requirement of cigarette companies to put graphic images on their cigarette packets. The health visitors have a range of posters and leaflets displayed, along with photographs of lungs diseased with cancer. They also have some information and samples of products available to help people stop smoking, for example, chewing gum, patches, pretend cigarettes and other nicotine replacement therapies. All the leaflets are printed in a range of different languages, for example, Urdu, Gujarati, Chinese and Polish. As members of the public walk past the stand, the health visitors stop them and ask if they smoke, would like some more information or would like to attend a workshop to help them stop smoking.

Abigail

Abigail is 12 years of age and has just started Year 8 at school. The school nurse has just been into the class to talk about the new HPV immunization that will protect girls against certain types of cervical cancer. She has discussed all the benefits of the vaccination and given Abigail a leaflet for her to take home to discuss with her parents.

The following week Abigail tells the nurse that she would like the vaccination but her parents do not want her to have it. The nurse suggests that she can meet with Abigail's parents to discuss the benefits but, until Abigail is 16 and she is legally entitled to make her own decisions, the nurse has to respect the parents' wishes.

Mrs Rashid

Mrs Rashid has recently celebrated her fiftieth birthday and in the post this morning she received an invitation to the local hospital for breast screening. The letter contained a leaflet entitled 'Breast screening – The facts'. The leaflet informed Mrs Rashid that now she is 50 she will be invited for breast screening every three years because this is one of the best ways of detecting breast cancer. The leaflet reassured Mrs Rashid that all the staff at the breast screening clinic are female and that there will also be a translator available if she does not understand English. The leaflet and letter were written in both English and Urdu.

Care values and health promotion

The aim of this activity is to encourage students to consider how care values can be put into practice through the use of care principles in the promotion and support of health improvement.

Resources

- 'Providing support' case studies.
- PowerPoint® 5.8 or a whiteboard.

Instructions

1. Write each of the five care principles listed below on the board or display **PowerPoint® 5.8**:
    - promotion of choice
    - respecting identity and culture
    - empowerment
    - promoting independence
    - respecting individual right to choice

2. Divide the class up into groups. Then, photocopy and hand out the case studies on 'Providing support'.

3. Ask the groups to read the case studies carefully and to decide which care values each one is demonstrating. The groups should make notes, giving reasons for their decisions.

Plenary

Discuss the results of each group. Point out that each case study may demonstrate more than one care value. You could then ask the groups to explain why they think the case studies show evidence of their chosen care value(s).

Health promotion

The aim of this activity is to introduce the students to the basic principles of a health promotion campaign and also encourage learners to think about professional support that is available.

Resources

- PowerPoint® 5.9.
- For display board:
  - a selection of sugar paper/coloured card/coloured paper
  - scissors
  - colouring pencils/felt tips
  - access to IT facilities if possible
  - non-toxic glue
  - board stapler/reusable adhesive.
- For leaflets/posters:
  - paper/card
  - colouring pencils/felt tips
  - access to IT facilities if possible.

Instructions

1. Look at the 'Ten tips for better health' on **PowerPoint® 5.9**. These 'ten tips' were offered by the Chief Medical Officer, Liam Donaldson in the White Paper 'Saving Lives: Our Healthier Nation' (1999). Discuss each point, in turn, with the students.

2. **Either:**
   a) split the class into two or three groups (depending on numbers and available display boards). Each group should select one of the 'Ten tips' and design a 'Health promotion display board' based on their chosen tip;

   or: b) working individually, each student could design a leaflet or poster that addresses one of the 'Ten tips'.

3. Encourage students to include some information about:
   - the benefits of making the right choice
   - professional support available to help make the lifestyle change.

Does health promotion really work?

The aim of this activity is to encourage discussion around the question of how successful health promotion really is. It should also increase students' awareness of reasons why health promotion may not be successful and enable them to practise interpreting data.

Resources

- Photocopies of the 'BMI and smoking statistics' information sheet. (You may wish to laminate them for future use.)

Instructions

1. Divide the class up into groups.

2. Give each group a copy of the information sheet 'BMI and smoking statistics'.

3. Start the session off by asking the class as a whole to consider the trends shown by the graphs. Ask questions such as:
   - 'What does the graph tell us about the body mass of the population over the five years?'
   - 'What does the graph tell us about smoking trends over the 31 years?'

4. Then, ask the students to discuss the following in their groups:
   - 'What health promotion campaigns are you aware of that address the two issues discussed?' (They may need to undertake some research to find this out.)
   - 'How successful have they been?'
   - 'Give some reasons why you think the campaigns have or have not been successful.'

Plenary

Bring the whole group together. Ask individuals to read out their answers and then discuss these as a class.

Suggested answers can be found on **PowerPoint® 5.10**.

BMI and smoking statistics

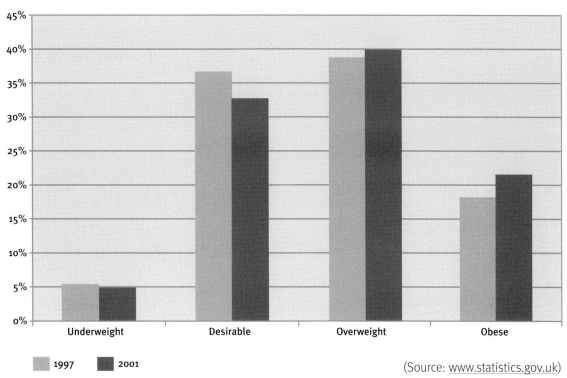

Percentage Change in Body Mass 1997–2001

1997   2001

(Source: www.statistics.gov.uk)

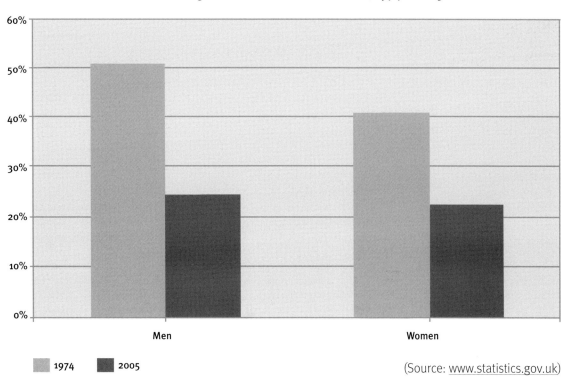

Percentage of male and female smokers, 1974 & 2005

1974   2005

(Source: www.statistics.gov.uk)

Folens' Practice Test for Edexcel

Time allowed: 1 hour 15 minutes

Instructions

- Use **BLACK** ink or ballpoint pen.

- Answer **ALL** the questions.

- Answer the questions in the space provided – there may be more space than you need.

Information

- The total mark for this paper is 70.

- The marks for **each** question are shown in brackets at the end of each question or part question – use this as a guide as to how much time to spend on each question.

- Questions marked with an **asterisk** (*) are ones where the quality of your written communication will be assessed. You should take particular care with your spelling, punctuation and grammar, as well as your clarity of expression, when answering these questions.

Advice

- Read each question carefully and make sure you know what you have to do before starting your answer.

- Keep an eye on the time.

- Try to answer every question.

- Check your answers if you have time at the end.

Answer ALL questions.

1. Paul is in his early thirties. He is married and has a daughter, Katie. Until recently, Paul worked as a long-distance lorry driver but three weeks ago he was made redundant. Six months ago, following a long illness, Paul's mother died. Paul misses her a great deal. He made an appointment to see his GP because he had been feeling very low following the death of his mother and then losing his job. The GP felt that Paul was suffering from depression and suggested that counselling might help. He asked Paul if he would like to be referred.

   a) From the information given about Paul, identify:

   (i) one **expected** life event

   ....

   (1)

   (ii) one **unexpected** life event

   ....

   (1)

   b) Identify and describe **one** care value that is being applied by the doctor.

   ....

   ....

   ....

   ....

   ....

   ....

   ....

   ....

   (4)

c) Why is it important for professionals to maintain confidentiality when working with Paul?

....

....

....

....

....

....

....

(4)

d) Explain the effects that unexpected life events can have on an individual's social development.

....

....

....

....

....

....

....

....

....

(5)

Total for Question 1 = 15 marks

2. Katie, Paul's daughter, is six and attends Riverside Infant School. Katie has cerebral palsy and can only walk with a special frame. She needs special equipment to enable her to write and also to eat her lunch. Kerry is a classroom assistant who helps Katie when she is at school. She encourages her to join in activities with the other children and makes sure the other children include Katie in their games. Katie loves school and has lots of friends. Last week she was given a 'Merit' prize because she had worked so hard. Katie has a positive self-concept.

a) From the information given above, identify **three** factors that may account for Katie's positive self-concept.

1 ....

....

2 ....

....

3 ....

.... (3)

b) From the information given, identify:

(i) **one** of Katie's **physical** needs

....

.... (1)

(ii) **one** of Katie's **social** needs

....

.... (1)

GCSE Health & Social Care © Folens (copiable page)

c) Describe **two** ways in which staff at the school may meet Katie's **physical** needs.

1 ....

....

....

....

2 ....

....

....

.... (4)

d) *Kerry, the classroom assistant, encourages Katie to do as much as she can by herself, even when she finds it hard. This promotes Katie's independence and helps her to feel empowered. Explain **two** possible benefits of empowerment on Katie's emotional development.

....

....

....

....

....

....

....

....

....

....

....

.... (6)

e) *Discuss how care workers may prevent discrimination occurring at Riverside Infant School.

....

....

....

....

....

....

....

....

....

....

....

....

....

....

....

....

....

....

.... (10)

Total for Question 2 = 25 marks

GCSE Health & Social Care © Folens (copiable page)

3. Mr Sutcliffe is Paul's father. He is 72 years of age and since his wife died six months ago, he has started drinking beer on a more regular basis. He told Paul that he is drinking because he is very lonely. Paul has arranged for his father to attend a day centre where he can meet other people of his own age. The day centre runs activities throughout the day, such as arts and crafts, movement to music and word game competitions. They also organize day trips to local places of interest.

a) Which life stage is Mr Sutcliffe in?

....

.... (1)

b) Identify **one** lifestyle choice that Mr Sutcliffe has made.

....

.... (1)

c) Explain why it is important for Mr Sutcliffe to have the opportunity to join in activities.

....

....

....

....

....

....

....

.... (4)

GCSE Health & Social Care © Folens (copiable page)

d) *Describe **two** ways in which Mr Sutcliffe's lifestyle choices may affect his
   health and well-being.

   1 ....

   ....

   ....

   ....

   ....

   ....

   2 ....

   ....

   ....

   ....

   ....

   ....   (6)

GCSE Health & Social Care   © Folens (copiable page)

e) *Discuss how the activities provided at the day centre might meet Mr
    Sutcliffe's needs.

....

....

....

....

....

....

....

....

....

....

....

....

....

....

.... (8)

GCSE Health & Social Care   © Folens (copiable page)

f) *The care workers at the day centre decide to give Mr Sutcliffe some leaflets with information about the dangers of drinking.

Discuss the usefulness of health promotion material, for example, a leaflet, in helping Mr Sutcliffe adopt a healthier lifestyle.

....

....

....

....

....

....

....

....

....

....

....

....

....

....

....

....

....

....

....

.... (10)

Total for Question 3 = 30 marks

TOTAL FOR PAPER = 70 MARKS

GCSE **Health & Social Care**   © Folens (copiable page)